RED READER™

Romeo & Juliet

Annotated by John A. Price
Edited by Kara L. Quinn
Foreword by Judy Almeranti

TEACHER'S DISCOVERY™

ISBN: 0-7560-0150-1

Birth of the *Red Reader*™

Foreword

From the hallowed Globe Theatre to New York City stages, then on to big screens, and numerous smaller stages across the globe, and stored in personal PCs – William Shakespeare's monumental play *Romeo and Juliet* has weathered every form of translation.

Red Reader™ was conceived with the directive, "Find a starving actor/literary Shakespearean groupie, get 'em to translate R & J so kids who grew up on MTV™ can understand what the heck Shakespeare is saying…and make it fun!"

Enter Kara Quinn – young, gorgeous, blond, married to her Romeo Chris, dog-lover, lover of all things fast (as in fast-food), and previously a Shakespeare hatah! Ensconced in her cubicle, e-mailing Shakespeare expert hopefuls, reading endless submissions, then gleefully, happily announcing she had discovered her annotator – "He makes me laugh, and for the first time I understand what Shakespeare was trying to tell his audience!" Kara joyfully skips to her laptop, and spends the next months reading the hip hop style translations of John A. Price that reveal new worlds to her:

> "What man art thou that thus bescreen'd in night
> So stumblest on my counsel?"   (Price translates – Who 'dat?)

We're not really certain that Price was a starving actor, but he worked at being one for 18 years. He's really literate – has an M.F.A. in Theatre Education from Boston University, has presented and published articles on Shakespeare, post-modern literary theory and new ways to access Shakespeare's language. Did I mention Director as well?

We were impressed!

Now, pop yourself up some popcorn, grab a box of tissues, settle in your beanbag chair, and dig in to Shakespeare's world – his version – and one funny and literate man's take on perhaps the world's most famous love story ever told – *Romeo and Juliet*. You'll laugh, you'll cry. You'll even learn something!

Dramatis Personae
(Shakespeare's Peeps)

THE MONTAGUES

LORD MONTAGUE - Romeo's pop, but not a major player in this play; hates Lord Capulet.

LADY MONTAGUE - Romeo's mom, even fewer lines than pops here.

ROMEO - A 14-year-old lovesick dude in love with being in love; Lord Montague's only son.

BENVOLIO (Benny) - Romeo's cousin and homey.

BALTHASAR - Romeo's boy who doesn't come in until late in the play.

ABRAHAM - Montague's servant who fights for the Montague gang.

THE CAPULETS

LORD CAPULET - Juliet's pop and a straight-up control freak.

LADY CAPULET - Juliet's mom and a woman who doesn't understand teenagers - who does?

JULIET - 13 years old, Lord Capulet's only daughter, and Romeo's eventual main-squeeze.

TYBALT - A master swordsman with a bad temper and a short fuse - a bad combination.

NURSE - Juliet's maid with a mouth like a sailor.

PETER - The Nurse's servant and so dumb he can't read his own name.

SAMPSON - Capulet's servant who fights for the Capulet gang.

GREGORY - Capulet's servant and Montague-hatah who fights for the Capulet gang.

OTHER PEEPS

PRINCE ESCALUS - The ruler of Verona.

MERCUTIO - Romeo's best bud who is in love with words and the sound of his own voice.

FRIAR LAURENCE (FATHER LARRY) - The priest who is friends with Romeo and tries to help, but can't.

COUNTY PARIS - Wants to marry Juliet and cuts a deal with Lord Capulet for her.

APOTHECARY - A 14th-century drug dealer who sells to Romeo.

Romeo and Juliet
∼ Act I, Scene I ∼
Scene Synopsis

The servants of the two feuding families, the Montagues and Capulets, dis' each other 'til a fight breaks out. Prince Escalus goes off on both families, warning that if another fight occurs, heads will roll.

MacDaddy Romeo (or so he thinks!) is bummed about Rosaline, a babe he wants to hook up with, because she ignores him. His cousin Benvolio (Benny) encourages him to get his groove on elsewhere.

Prologue

Enter CHORUS

CHORUS

Two households, both alike in dignity,
In fair Verona, where we lay our scene,
From ancient grudge break to new mutiny,
Where civil blood makes civil hands unclean.
From forth the fatal loins of these two foes
A pair of star-cross'd lovers take their life;
Whose misadventured piteous overthrows
Doth with their death bury their parents' strife.
The fearful passage of their death-mark'd love,
And the continuance of their parents' rage,
Which, but their children's end, nought could remove,
Is now the two hours' traffic of our stage;
The which if you with patient ears attend,
What here shall miss, our toil shall strive to mend.

Exeunt

Romeo and Juliet (1595) begins with a sonnet. Shakespeare's possible allusion, or reference, to the source he used for this play: Arthur Brooke's long narrative poem, *The Tragical History of Romeus and Juliet* (1562).

WAIT!!!! Hold up. . .they die?? Great, six lines into this thing and this Chorus guy gives away the ending. Thanks.

Shakespeare prepares us for the tragedy with the meaning and style of the language. Notice the repetition of "two" (two households, two foes, two hours), the juxtaposition, or contrast, of images (civil blood/civil hands), and themes reinforced by sound ("doth with their death").

Scene I

Verona. A public place.

Enter SAMPSON and GREGORY, of the house of Capulet, armed with swords and bucklers.

SAMPSON

Gregory, o' my word, we'll not carry coals.

GREGORY

No, for then we should be colliers.

SAMPSON

I mean, an we be in choler, we'll draw.

GREGORY

Ay, while you live, draw your neck out o' the collar.

SAMPSON

I strike quickly, being moved.

GREGORY

But thou art not quickly moved to strike.

SAMPSON

A dog of the house of Montague moves me.

A buckler is a small shield. That's probably where cowboys got the idea for their belt buckles. Have you seen the size of those things?

Although these servants cause the first fight, Shakespeare uses these low-class characters for comedy as well—a technique Elizabethan audiences would have known and appreciated.

Notice the servants' wordplay with puns on the word "coals"—
"carry coals": to bear insults,
"colliers": coal workers,
"in choler": angry,
"collar": a hangman's noose.

Sampson must be allergic to dogs.

GREGORY

To move is to stir; and to be valiant is to stand:
therefore, if thou art moved, thou runn'st away.

SAMPSON

A dog of that house shall move me to stand: I will
take the wall of any man or maid of Montague's.

GREGORY

That shows thee a weak slave; for the weakest goes
to the wall.

SAMPSON

'Tis true; and therefore women, being the weaker vessels,
are ever thrust to the wall: therefore I will push
Montague's men from the wall, and thrust his maids
to the wall.

GREGORY

The quarrel is between our masters and us their men.

SAMPSON

'Tis all one, I will show myself a tyrant: when I
have fought with the men, I will be cruel with the
maids, I will cut off their heads.

GREGORY

The heads of the maids?

SAMPSON

Ay, the heads of the maids, or their maidenheads;
take it in what sense thou wilt.

GREGORY

They must take it in sense that feel it.

SAMPSON

Me they shall feel while I am able to stand: and
'tis known I am a pretty piece of flesh.

GREGORY

'Tis well thou art not fish; if thou hadst, thou
hadst been poor John. Draw thy tool! here comes
two of the house of Montagues.

Enter two other SERVINGMEN, ABRAHAM and BALTHASAR

SAMPSON

My naked weapon is out: quarrel, I will back thee.

GREGORY

How! turn thy back and run?

SAMPSON

Fear me not.

GREGORY

No, marry; I fear thee!

SAMPSON

Let us take the law of our sides; let them begin.

Again, wordplay with "wall."

During this era, the center of the street was used for drainage; therefore, the wall, the cleanest place, was often reserved for nobility to walk.

To have one's back to the wall; to be threatened or scared.

Here Sampson and Gregory begin bawdy (sexual) references. Sampson implies a violent attack or rape.

Avoid any book entitled, *Sampson's Advice on Dating*.

Cut off their heads? Is that before or after dinner and a movie?

Again with the bawdy twins! "Maidenhead": virginity.

Yeah, Gregory! Master of the Obvious.

A rather high opinion of himself.

The pun on flesh/fish is underscored by the "poor John" insult. "Poor John" was a poor quality salted/dried fish.

I hope he's talking about his sword.

There's nothing quite like teammates fighting (see the '01-'02 Minnesota Vikings).

GREGORY

I will frown as I pass by, and let them take it as
they list.

SAMPSON

Nay, as they dare. I will bite my thumb at them;
which is disgrace to them, if they bear it.

"Bite my thumb" is the
Elizabethan version of flip-off or
"giving the bird."

ABRAHAM

Do you bite your thumb at us, sir?

SAMPSON

I do bite my thumb, sir.

ABRAHAM

Do you bite your thumb at us, sir?

SAMPSON

[Aside to GREGORY.] Is the law of our side, if I say
ay?

Shouldn't he have thought of this
before starting the fight?

GREGORY

No.

SAMPSON

No, sir, I do not bite my thumb at you, sir, but I
bite my thumb, sir.

GREGORY

Do you quarrel, sir?

ABRAHAM

Quarrel sir! no, sir.

SAMPSON

But if you do, sir, I am for you: I serve as good a man as you.

ABRAHAM

No better.

SAMPSON

Well, sir.

Enter BENVOLIO

GREGORY

Say 'better.' here comes one of my master's kinsmen.

Translation: "Go ahead, here
comes someone who isn't a
coward and knows how to fight."

SAMPSON

Yes, better, sir.

ABRAHAM

You lie.

SAMPSON

Draw, if you be men. Gregory, remember thy swashing blow.
[They fight.]

An agile sword move (or do
they rapidly begin to sketch
each other?).

BENVOLIO

Part, fools!
Put up your swords; you know not what you do.

Benny is Romeo's cousin and is
usually the voice of reason for the
emotional Romeo.

Enter TYBALT

That's it Benny! Control violence
with violence. Two wrongs make
a right, right?

TYBALT

What, art thou drawn among these heartless hinds?
Turn thee, Benvolio, look upon thy death.

BENVOLIO

I do but keep the peace? put up thy sword,
Or manage it to part these men with me.

TYBALT

What, drawn, and talk of peace? I hate the word,
As I hate hell, all Montagues, and thee:
Have at thee, coward!
[*They fight.*]

Irony: holding a sword, yet talking of peace, recalls the civil hands/civil blood of the Prologue.

Enter an OFFICER and three or four CITIZENS with clubs or partisans

(Tybalt and Hell: Luhrmann's '96 film had Tybalt dressed in a devil's costume.)

OFFICER

Clubs, bills, and partisans! strike! beat them down!

Clubs, bills, and partisans (or halberds) were all hand-held weapons.

CITIZENS

Down with the Capulets! down with the Montagues!

The citizens express frustration over the feuding and violence.

Enter CAPULET in his gown, and LADY CAPULET

Capulet, always dressed for battle.

CAPULET

What noise is this? Give me my long sword, ho!

LADY CAPULET

A crutch, a crutch! why call you for a sword?

No, Lord Capulet is not calling his wife a "ho." An exclamatory (like "Hey!") often used to get someone's attention.

CAPULET

My sword, I say! Old Montague is come,
And flourishes his blade in spite of me.

Notice that the ladies are calling for peace.

Enter MONTAGUE and LADY MONTAGUE

Flourishing or showing a sword was a challenge to the enemy - the fight is on.

MONTAGUE

Thou villain Capulet,–Hold me not, let me go.

LADY MONTAGUE

Thou shalt not stir one foot to seek a foe.

Enter PRINCE ESCALUS with his train

PRINCE

Rebellious subjects, enemies to peace,
Profaners of this neighbour-stained steel,--
Will they not hear? What, ho! you men, you beasts
That quench the fire of your pernicious rage
With purple fountains issuing from your veins,
On pain of torture, from those bloody hands
Throw your mistemper'd weapons to the ground,
And hear the sentence of your moved Prince.
Three civil brawls, bred of an airy word,
By thee, old Capulet, and Montague,
Have thrice disturb'd the quiet of our streets,
And made Verona's ancient citizens
Cast by their grave beseeming ornaments,
To wield old partisans, in hands as old,
Canker'd with peace, to part your canker'd hate:
If ever you disturb our streets again,
Your lives shall pay the forfeit of the peace.
For this time, all the rest depart away:

Like the juxtaposition of images in the Prologue, the Prince uses the same wordplay to make his point to the warring families; Rebellious subjects, men/beasts, canker'd peace/canker'd hate.

The Prince describes Verona as a retirement home. No wonder he's mad about the disturbance. The Montagues and Capulets probably play loud music, too.

"Fight again, and I'll kill you!"

You Capulet; shall go along with me:
And, Montague, come you this afternoon,
To know our farther pleasure in this case,
To old Freetown, our common judgement-place.
Once more, on pain of death, all men depart.

Exeunt all but MONTAGUE, LADY MONTAGUE, and BENVOLIO

MONTAGUE
  Who set this ancient quarrel new abroach?
  Speak, nephew, were you by when it began?

BENVOLIO
  Here were the servants of your adversary,
  And yours, close fighting ere I did approach:
  I drew to part them: in the instant came
  The fiery Tybalt, with his sword prepared,
  Which, as he breathed defiance to my ears,
  He swung about his head and cut the winds,
  Who nothing hurt withal hiss'd him in scorn:
  While we were interchanging thrusts and blows,
  Came more and more and fought on part and part,
  Till the Prince came, who parted either part.

LADY MONTAGUE
  O, where is Romeo? saw you him today?
  Right glad I am he was not at this fray.

BENVOLIO
  Madam, an hour before the worshipp'd sun
  Peer'd forth the golden window of the east,
  A troubled mind drave me to walk abroad;
  Where, underneath the grove of sycamore
  That westward rooteth from this city side,
  So early walking did I see your son:
  Towards him I made, but he was ware of me
  And stole into the covert of the wood:
  I, measuring his affections by my own,
  Which then most sought, where most might not be found,
  Being one too many by my weary self,
  Pursued my humour not pursuing his,
  And gladly shunn'd who gladly fled from me.

MONTAGUE
  Many a morning hath he there been seen,
  With tears augmenting the fresh morning's dew.
  Adding to clouds more clouds with his deep sighs;
  But all so soon as the all-cheering sun
  Should in the farthest east begin to draw
  The shady curtains from Aurora's bed,
  Away from light steals home my heavy son,
  And private in his chamber pens himself,
  Shuts up his windows, locks fair daylight out
  And makes himself an artificial night:
  Black and portentous must this humour prove,
  Unless good counsel may the cause remove.

Just in case they'd forgotten.

Benny offers the cool, rational, and blameless explanation. Translation: always cover your butt!

Tybalt "cut the winds"? That must have been embarrassing for him. No wonder he's so angry: it's a gastrointestinal problem.

That Romeo "was not at this fray" (the fight) emphasizes his "in-love-with-love" character. He is a foil, or direct opposite, to the character of Tybalt.

Romeo's love-torn emotions and eventual maturity are two examples that critics point to when claiming *Romeo and Juliet* as a young man's play. Written when Shakespeare was about thirty, the play glorifies ideal love.

With his explanation of Romeo's melancholy behavior, Montague introduces Shakespeare's use of light/dark imagery. Light, the most frequent image found in the Bible, typically refers to goodness, purity, and all things positive; dark, by contrast, refers to negative traits associated with night, black, or the devil, the Prince of Darkness.

BENVOLIO

    My noble uncle, do you know the cause?

MONTAGUE

    I neither know it nor can learn of him.

BENVOLIO

    Have you importuned him by any means?

MONTAGUE

    Both by myself and many other friends:
    But he, his own affections' counsellor,
    Is to himself--I will not say how true--
    But to himself so secret and so close,
    So far from sounding and discovery,
    As is the bud bit with an envious worm,
    Ere he can spread his sweet leaves to the air,
    Or dedicate his beauty to the sun.
    Could we but learn from whence his sorrows grow.
    We would as willingly give cure as know.

Enter ROMEO

BENVOLIO

    See, where he comes: so please you, step aside;
    I'll know his grievance, or be much denied.

MONTAGUE

    I would thou wert so happy by thy stay,
    To hear true shrift. Come, madam, let's away.

Exeunt MONTAGUE and LADY MONTAGUE

BENVOLIO

    Good morrow, cousin.

ROMEO

    Is the day so young?

BENVOLIO

    But new struck nine.

ROMEO

    Ay me! sad hours seem long.
    Was that my father that went hence so fast?

BENVOLIO

    It was. What sadness lengthens Romeo's hours?

ROMEO

    Not having that, which, having, makes them short.

BENVOLIO

    In love?

ROMEO

    Out--

BENVOLIO

    Of love?

ROMEO

    Out of her favour, where I am in love.

Commentary (right column):

No, but I bet Benny can guess. Can you say, L-O-V-E?

Of course, Dad wouldn't know.

Translation: Have you spied on him?

While Montague uses some wonderful imagery here, comparing Romeo's silence to nature's mysteries, his answer is: "I don't know."

Shakespeare's light/dark images were realized in Zeffirelli's '68 film as Romeo entered alone, walking in the shadows created by the walls of the city.

Shakespeare emphasizes the boys' relationship through language.

Benny and Romeo share the rhythms of the iambic pentameter or blank verse. Remember, this is "poetic drama."

These first two lines combine to create one ten-beat line of dramatic verse. The whole play is also one long poem, with prose passages assigned to less-important dialogue.

Notice the emerging theme of opposites: slow/fast, not having/having, in/out.

Cover your ears! The boys are using four-letter words.

BENVOLIO

Alas, that love, so gentle in his view,
Should be so tyrannous and rough in proof!

ROMEO

Alas, that love, whose view is muffled still,
Should, without eyes, see pathways to his will!
Where shall we dine? O me! What fray was here?
Yet tell me not, for I have heard it all.
Here's much to do with hate, but more with love.
Why, then, O brawling love! O loving hate!
O anything, of nothing first create!
O heavy lightness! serious vanity!
Misshapen chaos of well-seeming forms!
Feather of lead, bright smoke, cold fire, sick health!
Still-waking sleep, that is not what it is!
This love feel I, that feel no love in this.
Dost thou not laugh?

BENVOLIO

No, coz, I rather weep.

ROMEO

Good heart, at what?

BENVOLIO

At thy good heart's oppression.

ROMEO

Why, such is love's transgression.
Griefs of mine own lie heavy in my breast,
Which thou wilt propagate, to have it prest
With more of thine: this love that thou hast shown
Doth add more grief to too much of mine own.
Love is a smoke raised with the fume of sighs;
Being purged, a fire sparkling in lovers' eyes;
Being vex'd a sea nourish'd with lovers' tears:
What is it else? a madness most discreet,
A choking gall and a preserving sweet.
Farewell, my coz.

BENVOLIO

Soft! I will go along;
An if you leave me so, you do me wrong.

ROMEO

Tut, I have lost myself; I am not here;
This is not Romeo, he's some other where.

BENVOLIO

Tell me in sadness, who is that you love?

ROMEO

What, shall I groan and tell thee?

BENVOLIO

Groan! why, no.
But sadly tell me who.

Benny makes light of Romeo's confession.

The "he" mentioned is Cupid, often depicted with a blindfold. That love is blind frustrates Romeo as he quickly changes the subject.

Any more proof needed of the interrelationship of opposites theme?

Is this dude confused, or what?

Yes, you're a comedian. Are you seeing a doctor?

Uh, Benny. . .I think that's pronounced *depression*.

Notice how Romeo uses rhyming verse when speaking of love.

"An" in Renaissance texts is used variously: sometimes as a short form of "and," in the interest of mimicking the sound of actual speech; sometimes as "if." As in most variant usages in Shakespeare, the context of the passage guides usage.

Benny's a good friend to not suggest medication here, or wherever Romeo is.

The tension begins.

Why is he avoiding a direct answer?

Uh-oh, Benny gets a little worried.

ROMEO

    Bid a sick man in sadness make his will:
    Ah, word ill urged to one that is so ill!
    In sadness, cousin, I do love a woman.

BENVOLIO

    I aim'd so near, when I supposed you loved.

ROMEO

    A right good markman! And she's fair I love.

BENVOLIO

    A right fair mark, fair coz, is soonest hit.

ROMEO

    Well, in that hit you miss: she'll not be hit
    With Cupid's arrow; she hath Dian's wit;
    And, in strong proof of chastity well arm'd,
    From love's weak childish bow she lives unharm'd.
    She will not stay the siege of loving terms,
    Nor bide th' encounter of assailing eyes,
    Nor ope her lap to saint-seducing gold:
    O, she is rich in beauty, only poor,
    That when she dies with beauty dies her store.

BENVOLIO

    Then she hath sworn that she will still live chaste?

ROMEO

    She hath, and in that sparing makes huge waste,
    For beauty starved with her severity
    Cuts beauty off from all posterity.
    She is too fair, too wise, wisely too fair,
    To merit bliss by making me despair:
    She hath forsworn to love, and in that vow
    Do I live dead that live to tell it now.

BENVOLIO

    Be ruled by me, forget to think of her.

ROMEO

    O, teach me how I should forget to think.

BENVOLIO

    By giving liberty unto thine eyes;
    Examine other beauties.

ROMEO

    'Tis the way
    To call hers exquisite, in question more:
    These happy masks that kiss fair ladies' brows
    Being black put us in mind they hide the fair;
    He that is strucken blind cannot forget
    The precious treasure of his eyesight lost:
    Show me a mistress that is passing fair,
    What doth her beauty serve, but as a note
    Where I may read who pass'd that passing fair?
    Farewell: thou canst not teach me to forget.

Margin notes:

Benny heaves a deep sigh of relief.

Yeah, easy for you to say NOW!

Cupid wordplay with aiming and targets.

Ah, Benny gets bawdy!

More mythology: Diana, the goddess who advised chastity.

Zeus seduced (that rhymes!) Diana with a shower of gold. Hey, a girl's gotta shop.

(What did I just say?)

Both Benny and later Mercutio underestimate Romeo's heartsick condition.

Sure, easy for you to say.

Romeo explains that seeing other women would just emphasize Rosaline's beauty to him.

Introduction of a key theme: masking or disguising one's true identity.

Translation: He's got it bad.

BENVOLIO

    I'll pay that doctrine, or else die in debt.

I'll change your mind, or die trying.

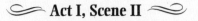

Act I, Scene II

Scene Synopsis

    The County Paris (a count: like the annoying *Sesame Street* character or Count Dracula - Paris isn't evil, but he is annoying) asks Lord Capulet (Juliet's father - and just as annoying as Paris) if he can marry Juliet. She is not old enough (13), but if she approves of Paris, he'll look into it.

    The Capulets are throwing a party (actually an elaborate masquerade ball); Romeo and Benny intercept the invitation and learn that Rosaline will be there. Romeo swears his undying love for Rosaline (until he sees Juliet!).

Scene II

A street.

Enter CAPULET, COUNTY PARIS, and SERVANT

CAPULET

    But Montague is bound as well as I,
    In penalty alike; and 'tis not hard, I think,
    For men so old as we to keep the peace.

> Capulet is in a difficult situation: the Prince has threatened his life and Paris wants his Juliet for his bride.

PARIS

    Of honourable reckoning are you both;
    And pity 'tis you lived at odds so long.
    But now, my lord, what say you to my suit?

> That's too bad about the fighting. So, when can I have Juliet?

CAPULET

    But saying o'er what I have said before:
    My child is yet a stranger in the world;
    She hath not seen the change of fourteen years,
    Let two more summers wither in their pride,
    Ere we may think her ripe to be a bride.

> Marriage was a matter of business in Renaissance Italy. Negotiations for the dowry (bride's family money) could last months - even years. And the official marriage documents could go on for blocks!

PARIS

    Younger than she are happy mothers made.

CAPULET

    And too soon marr'd are those so early made.
    Earth hath swallow'd all my hopes but she,
    She is the hopeful lady of my earth:
    My will to her consent is but a part;
    An she agree, within her scope of choice
    Lies my consent and fair according voice.
    This night I hold an old accustom'd feast,
    Whereto I have invited many a guest,
    Such as I love; and you, among the store,
    One more, most welcome, makes my number more.
    At my poor house look to behold this night
    Earth-treading stars that make dark heaven light:

> Note the rhymed verse and subject of the following speech: love.

> Capulet, although headstrong to a fault, will not be easily persuaded by Paris.

> What is it with the young men in this play? Okay, cold showers for all! Actually, youth impulsiveness is a key theme in this play about deeply flawed character.

> Capulet echoes Benny's speech to Romeo concerning other women and not rushing things.

Such comfort as do lusty young men feel
When well-apparell'd April on the heel
Of limping winter treads, even such delight
Among fresh female buds shall you this night
Inherit at my house; hear all, all see,
And like her most whose merit most shall be:
Which on more view of many, mine, being one,
May stand in number, though in reckoning none,
Come, go with me.

[To SERVANT, giving a paper.]

Go, sirrah, trudge about
Through fair Verona; find those persons out
Whose names are written there, and to them say,
My house and welcome on their pleasure stay.

Exeunt CAPULET and PARIS

SERVANT

Find them out whose names are written here! It is
written, that the shoemaker should meddle with his
yard, and the tailor with his last, the fisher with
his pencil, and the painter with his nets; but I am
sent to find those persons whose names are here
writ, and can never find what names the writing
person hath here writ. I must to the learned.--In good time.

Enter BENVOLIO and ROMEO

BENVOLIO

Tut, man, one fire burns out another's burning,
One pain is lessen'd by another's anguish;
Turn giddy, and be holp by backward turning;
One desperate grief cures with another's languish:
Take thou some new infection to thy eye,
And the rank poison of the old will die.

ROMEO

Your plantain leaf is excellent for that.

BENVOLIO

For what, I pray thee?

ROMEO

For your broken shin.

BENVOLIO

Why, Romeo, art thou mad?

ROMEO

Not mad, but bound more than a madman is;
Shut up in prison, kept without my food,
Whipp'd and tormented and--God-den, good fellow.

SERVANT

God gi' god-den. I pray, sir, can you read?

ROMEO

Ay, mine own fortune in my misery.

"Lusty young men" - there's an understatement.

What do you think? Consider the theme of the last two scenes and the tragic end to this play. Is Shakespeare advising young people to be cautious with love?

Time for a little comic relief. Elizabethans would have immediately recognized this comic setup: servants could not read.

The servant's confusion about occupations and tools of the trade is typical among Shakespeare's clowns and low characters.

Benny and Romeo continue their conversation concerning the need to consider love's options before committing oneself so soon.

Love as an infection - Benny jokes as Romeo alludes to the Elizabethan use of leaves and herbs for medicinal purposes.

Translation: "You're bothering me like a blister."

"God-den": good evening.

SERVANT

Perhaps you have learned it without book: but, I
pray, can you read anything you see?

ROMEO

Ay, if I know the letters and the language.

Romeo's joke goes unnoticed.

SERVANT

Ye say honestly: rest you merry!

Misunderstanding, the servant
prepares to leave.

ROMEO

Stay, fellow; I can read.

[*Reads.*]

'Signior Martino and his wife and daughters;
County Anselmo and his beauteous sisters; the lady
widow of Vitruvio; Signior Placentio and his lovely
nieces; Mercutio and his brother Valentine; mine
uncle Capulet, his wife and daughters; my fair niece
Rosaline and Livia; Signior Valentio and his cousin
Tybalt, Lucio and the lively Helena.' A fair assembly.
Whither should they come?

Aha! A name he knows well!

SERVANT

Up.

ROMEO

Whither to supper?

SERVANT

To our house.

ROMEO

Whose house?

SERVANT

My master's.

ROMEO

Indeed, I should have ask'd you that before.

SERVANT

Now I'll tell you without asking: my master is the
great rich Capulet; and if you be not of the house
of Montagues, I pray, come and crush a cup of wine.
Rest you merry!

Romeo has asked three times.
A mainstay of Shakespearean
comedy: the clueless servant.

Exit

BENVOLIO

At this same ancient feast of Capulet's
Sups the fair Rosaline whom thou so loves,
With all the admired beauties of Verona:
Go thither; and, with unattainted eye,
Compare her face with some that I shall show,
And I will make thee think thy swan a crow.

Again, consider others before
making yourself sick over one
girl.

ROMEO

When the devout religion of mine eye
Maintains such falsehood, then turn tears to fires;
And these, who often drown'd could never die,
Transparent heretics, be burnt for liars!

A crow? And your girlfriend
would be. . . ? Notice our poet's
use of the rhymed couplet at
the end of a witty passage.

One fairer than my love! the all-seeing sun
Ne'er saw her match since first the world begun.

BENVOLIO

Tut, you saw her fair, none else being by,
Herself poised with herself in either eye:
But in that crystal scales let there be weigh'd
Your lady's love against some other maid
That I will show you shining at this feast,
And she shall scant show well that now seems best.

ROMEO

I'll go along, no such sight to be shown,
But to rejoice in splendor of mine own.

Exeunt

Romeo claims undying love for Rosaline. Wait until he sees Juliet - "the all-seeing sun" will be eclipsed.

Benny the prophet; what he predicts comes true. For Romeo, Juliet is l-o-v-e at first s-i-g-h-t.

O, ye of little faith!

Act I, Scene III

Scene Synopsis

Lady Capulet (Juliet's mom and clearly the brains of the family) tells Juliet of nerdy Paris' plans to marry her. Juliet politely refuses, but says she will be nice to Paris. Watch the Nurse - she's a trip!

Scene III
A room in Capulet's house.

Enter LADY CAPULET and NURSE

The Nurse is one of the most famous comic confidants in all of Shakespeare's plays. Like Romeo's friend Mercutio, the Nurse loves to hear herself talk. Too bad others don't feel the same way.

LADY CAPULET

Nurse, where's my daughter? call her forth to me.

NURSE

Now, by my maidenhead, at twelve year old,
I bade her come. What, lamb! what, ladybird!
God forbid! Where's this girl? What, Juliet!

Enter JULIET

JULIET

How now! who calls?

NURSE

Your mother.

JULIET

Madam, I am here.
What is your will?

LADY CAPULET

This is the matter:–Nurse, give leave awhile,
We must talk in secret:–Nurse, come back again;
I have remember'd me, thou's hear our counsel.
Thou know'st my daughter's of a pretty age.

Lady Capulet asks the Nurse to leave, then stay. There is tension between Lady Capulet and Juliet on the subject of marriage.

NURSE

Faith, I can tell her age unto an hour.

LADY CAPULET

She's not fourteen.

NURSE

 I'll lay fourteen of my teeth,--
 And yet, to my teen be it spoken, I have but four--
 She's not fourteen. How long is it now
 To Lammas-tide?

Veterinarians can tell a horse's age by its teeth.

LADY CAPULET

 A fortnight and odd days.

NURSE

 Even or odd, of all days in the year,
 Come Lammas Eve at night shall she be fourteen.
 Susan and she–God rest all Christian souls!--
 Were of an age: well, Susan is with God;
 She was too good for me: but, as I said,
 On Lammas Eve at night shall she be fourteen;
 That shall she, marry; I remember it well.
 'Tis since the earthquake now eleven years;
 And she was wean'd,--I never shall forget it,--
 Of all the days of the year, upon that day:
 For I had then laid wormwood to my dug,
 Sitting in the sun under the dovehouse wall;
 My lord and you were then at Mantua:--
 Nay, I do bear a brain:–but, as I said,
 When it did taste the wormwood on the nipple
 Of my dug and felt it bitter, pretty fool,
 To see it tetchy and fall out with the dug!
 Shake quoth the dovehouse: 'twas no need, I trow,
 To bid me trudge:
 And since that time it is eleven years;
 For then she could stand high-lone; nay, by th' rood,
 She could have run and waddled all about;
 For even the day before, she broke her brow:
 And then my husband–God be with his soul!
 A was a merry man–took up the child:
 'Yea,' quoth he, 'dost thou fall upon thy face?
 Thou wilt fall backward when thou hast more wit;
 Wilt thou not, Jule?' and, by my holidame,
 The pretty wretch left crying and said 'Ay.'
 To see, now, how a jest shall come about!
 I warrant, an I should live a thousand years,
 I never should forget it: 'Wilt thou not, Jule?' quoth he;
 And, pretty fool, it stinted and said 'Ay.'

The Nurse stops, starts, and repeats herself until Lady Capulet asks her to stop.

Here she embarrasses both Juliet and her mother by discussing in great detail her breast feeding and weaning of Juliet.

"rood": cross or crucifix on which Christ died. This is a sacred oath, common at this time.

The servant Nurse knows little of social etiquette. She laughs, recalling how the infant Juliet innocently answered "yes" to a sexual joke of "falling backward" (a maiden on her back).

LADY CAPULET

 Enough of this; I pray thee, hold thy peace.

NURSE

 Yes, madam: yet I cannot choose but laugh,
 To think it should leave crying and say 'Ay.'
 And yet, I warrant, it had upon its brow
 A bump as big as a young cockerel's stone;
 A perilous knock; and it cried bitterly:
 'Yea,' quoth my husband,'fall'st upon thy face?

And again, she repeats the same story. Enough already!

Thou wilt fall backward when thou comest to age;
Wilt thou not, Jule?' it stinted and said 'Ay.'

JULIET

And stint thou too, I pray thee, Nurse, say I.

NURSE

Peace, I have done. God mark thee to his grace!
Thou wast the prettiest babe that e'er I nursed:
An I might live to see thee married once,
I have my wish.

What part of shut up don't you understand?

Despite her talkativeness, it is clear that she loves Juliet.

LADY CAPULET

Marry, that 'marry' is the very theme
I came to talk of. Tell me, daughter Juliet,
How stands your disposition to be married?

Only a mother would ask a daughter her feelings on marriage. A father, seeking a business deal, tells the girl.

JULIET

It is an honour that I dream not of.

NURSE

An honour! were not I thine only nurse,
I would say thou hadst suck'd wisdom from thy teat.

She's not helping. And she's talking about her breasts again.

LADY CAPULET

Well, think of marriage now; younger than you,
Here in Verona, ladies of esteem,
Are made already mothers: by my count,
I was your mother much upon these years
That you are now a maid. Thus then in brief:
The valiant Paris seeks you for his love.

In the following exchange, Lady Capulet and the Nurse take turns trying to persuade Juliet to think about Paris as a husband.

NURSE

A man, young lady! lady, such a man
As all the world--why, he's a man of wax.

The Nurse focuses on Paris' looks. "Wax": as beautiful as a wax figure.

LADY CAPULET

Verona's summer hath not such a flower.

NURSE

Nay, he's a flower; in faith, a very flower.

Okay, Nurse - is he or isn't he a flower?

LADY CAPULET

What say you? can you love the gentleman?
This night you shall behold him at our feast;
Read o'er the volume of young Paris' face,
And find delight writ there with beauty's pen;
Examine every married lineament,
And see how one another lends content
And what obscured in this fair volume lies
Find written in the margent of his eyes.
This precious book of love, this unbound lover,
To beautify him, only lacks a cover:
The fish lives in the sea, and 'tis much pride
For fair without the fair within to hide:
That book in many's eyes doth share the glory,
That in gold clasps locks in the golden story;
So shall you share all that he doth possess,
By having him, making yourself no less.

While many literary critics comment on the book metaphor (volume, pen, content, margent-margin, and cover), the images also refer to the marriage contract benefiting the Capulet family (clasps, locks, golden, possess, and making yourself no less).

NURSE

    No less! nay, bigger; women grow by men.

LADY CAPULET

    Speak briefly, can you like of Paris' love?

JULIET

    I'll look to like, if looking liking move:
    But no more deep will I endart mine eye
    Than your consent gives strength to make it fly.

Enter a SERVINGMAN

SERVINGMAN

    Madam, the guests are come, supper served up, you
    called, my young lady asked for, the Nurse cursed in
    the pantry, and everything in extremity. I must
    hence to wait; I beseech you, follow straight.

LADY CAPULET

    We follow thee.

Exit SERVINGMAN

    Juliet, the County stays.

NURSE

    Go, girl, seek happy nights to happy days.

Exeunt

> Again, note the Nurse's low-end humor (her sexual punning).
>
> From breast feeding to pregnancy - a one-track mind (a very thin track - no train).
>
> Juliet acquiesces, but her speech is anything but confident concerning this arrangement with Paris.
>
> Translation: Downstairs the party is going to hell-in-a-handbag.
>
> Paris awaits you.
>
> Leonardo DiCaprio, dressed as a knight, created a pun with "night" in the '96 film.

Act I, Scene IV

Scene Synopsis

    Romeo and his home-peeps are on their way to the Capulets' party. The long-winded Mercutio entertains the guys with the now famous "Queen Mab" speech. Romeo grows bored with Mercutio and can't stop thinking about how his going to the party of his family's enemy is just wrong.

Scene IV
A street.

Enter ROMEO, MERCUTIO, BENVOLIO, with five or six
other MASKERS and TORCHBEARERS

ROMEO

    What, shall this speech be spoke for our excuse?
    Or shall we on without apology?

BENVOLIO

    The date is out of such prolixity:
    We'll have no Cupid hoodwink'd with a scarf,
    Bearing a Tartar's painted bow of lath,
    Scaring the ladies like a crowkeeper;
    Nor no without-book prologue, faintly spoke
    After the prompter, for our entrance:

> The boys (Montagues and friends) plan to crash the Capulets' party.
>
> Traditionally at masques the guests are announced as they arrive. Identity is revealed.
>
> Romeo asks if they'll follow tradition and announce themselves.
>
> Benny explains that introductions are out of fashion. They'll go and improvise ("without book") what they need.

But let them measure us by what they will;
We'll measure them a measure, and be gone.

ROMEO

Give me a torch: I am not for this ambling;
Being but heavy, I will bear the light.

MERCUTIO

Nay, gentle Romeo, we must have you dance.

ROMEO

Not I, believe me: you have dancing shoes
With nimble soles: I have a soul of lead
So stakes me to the ground I cannot move.

MERCUTIO

You are a lover; borrow Cupid's wings,
And soar with them above a common bound.

ROMEO

I am too sore enpierced with his shaft
To soar with his light feathers, and so bound,
I cannot bound a pitch above dull woe:
Under love's heavy burden do I sink.

MERCUTIO

And, to sink in it, should you burden love;
Too great oppression for a tender thing.

ROMEO

Is love a tender thing? it is too rough,
Too rude, too boisterous, and it pricks like thorn.

MERCUTIO

If love be rough with you, be rough with love;
Prick love for pricking, and you beat love down.
Give me a case to put my visage in:
A visor for a visor! what care I
What curious eye doth quote deformities?
Here are the beetle brows shall blush for me.

BENVOLIO

Come, knock and enter; and no sooner in,
But every man betake him to his legs.

ROMEO

A torch for me: let wantons light of heart
Tickle the senseless rushes with their heels,
For I am proverb'd with a grandsire phrase;
I'll be a candle-holder, and look on.
The game was ne'er so fair, and I am done.

MERCUTIO

Tut, dun's the mouse, the constable's own word:
If thou art dun, we'll draw thee from the mire
Of this sir-reverence love, wherein thou stick'st
Up to the ears. Come, we burn daylight, ho!

ROMEO

Nay, that's not so.

Wordplay: measure as to determine length/identity; a measure of music.

Romeo makes a pun on his mood and lack of participation in this prank.

Romeo anticipates rejection from Rosaline, and therefore sees no point in going to this party.

Wordplay: Romeo cynically plays on the words of his friends as they try to lift his spirits; "bound": tied down, to leap or hop. Many dances had leaping steps.

Mercutio mocks Romeo's mood by referring to him girlishly, as "tender."

Here Shakespeare uses the stock language of romantic love as a painful emotion. There is much of love's pain in the sonnets of Petrarch.

"Visor": a mask.
Here Shakespeare is building one of the play's overarching themes: identity (one's true self).

Romeo, still resisting the party, wants to stand to the side, watch, and hold candles.

"Dun's the mouse" was a proverb cautioning the hearer to be dark or hidden.

Wordplay: Mercutio plays on Romeo's done: finished, dun: dark.

Romeo - the wet blanket-Montague.

MERCUTIO

I mean, sir, in delay
We waste our lights in vain, like lamps by day.
Take our good meaning, for our judgement sits
Five times in that ere once in our five wits.

ROMEO

And we mean well in going to this masque;
But 'tis no wit to go.

MERCUTIO

Why, may one ask?

ROMEO

I dreamt a dream tonight.

MERCUTIO

And so did I.

ROMEO

Well, what was yours?

MERCUTIO

That dreamers often lie.

Wordplay: "lie" - to tell a falsehood; "lie" - to lie in bed

ROMEO

In bed asleep, while they do dream things true.

MERCUTIO

O, then, I see Queen Mab hath been with you.
She is the fairies' midwife, and she comes
In shape no bigger than an agate stone
On the forefinger of an alderman,
Drawn with a team of little atomies
Over men's noses as they lie asleep;
Her wagon spokes made of long spinners' legs,
The cover of the wings of grasshoppers,
The traces of the smallest spider web,
Her collars of the moonshine's wat'ry beams,
Her whip of cricket's bone, the lash of film,
Her wagoner a small grey-coated gnat,
Not half so big as a round little worm
Prick'd from the lazy finger of a maid;
Her chariot is an empty hazelnut
Made by the joiner squirrel or old grub,
Time out o' mind the fairies' coachmakers.
And in this state she gallops night by night
Through lovers' brains, and then they dream of love;
O'er courtiers' knees, that dream on curtsies straight,
O'er lawyers' fingers, who straight dream on fees,
O'er ladies ' lips, who straight on kisses dream,
Which oft the angry Mab with blisters plagues,
Because their breaths with sweetmeats tainted are:
Sometimes she gallops o'er a courtier's nose,
And then dreams he of smelling out a suit;
And sometime comes she with a tithe-pig's tail
Tickling a parson's nose as a lies asleep,

Mercutio's "Queen Mab" speech is second in recognition only to Juliet's "Romeo, Romeo, wherefore art thou Romeo?"

Elizabethans believed in the supernatural world of fairies. Many events, both good and bad, were blamed on their mysterious activities.

Written in approximately the same year, this speech sounds like a piece from Shakespeare's *A Midsummer Night's Dream*. The play, in part, takes place in a forest world ruled and inhabited by fairies and beset with amorous complications.

"suit": a petition to a monarch for a reward.

"tithe-pig": a pig due to a parson as a contribution.

Then dreams, he of another benefice:
Sometime she driveth o'er a soldier's neck,
And then dreams he of cutting foreign throats,
Of breaches, ambuscadoes, Spanish blades,
Of healths five fathom deep; and then anon
Drums in his ear, at which he starts and wakes,
And being thus frighted swears a prayer or two
And sleeps again. This is that very Mab
That plats the manes of horses in the night,
And bakes the elflocks in foul sluttish hairs,
Which once untangled, much misfortune bodes:
This is the hag, when maids lie on their backs,
That presses them and learns them first to bear,
Making them women of good carriage:
This is she–

"elflocks": matted hair often blamed on elves or "night-tripping fairies."

ROMEO

Peace, peace, Mercutio, peace!
Thou talk'st of nothing.

Translation: Stop! You're scaring me.

MERCUTIO

True, I talk of dreams,
Which are the children of an idle brain,
Begot of nothing but vain fantasy,
Which is as thin of substance as the air
And more inconstant than the wind, who wooes
Even now the frozen bosom of the north,
And, being anger'd, puffs away from thence,
Turning his face to the dew-dropping south.

BENVOLIO

This wind, you talk of, blows us from ourselves;
Supper is done, and we shall come too late.

ROMEO

I fear, too early: for my mind misgives
Some consequence yet hanging in the stars
Shall bitterly begin his fearful date
With this night's revels and expire the term
Of a despised life closed in my breast
By some vile forfeit of untimely death.
But he, that hath the steerage of my course,
Direct my sail! On, lusty gentlemen.

Romeo's speech foreshadows the tragic end of the play.

If you ever feel this way before going to an enemy's masquerade in Verona, learn from Romeo. Don't go!

BENVOLIO

Strike, drum.

Exeunt

Scene Synopsis

The Capulets greet the masked Romeo and his homies politely. While dancing, Romeo sees Juliet and is immediately in love; however, Tybalt, Juliet's cousin, (you know, the guy at school who always wears black and is angry at the world) overhears Romeo's questions about Juliet and wants to throw-down right there!

Not until after the party do R & J figure out that the person they just fell in love (or in lust) with is their family's enemy.

Scene V
A hall in Capulet's house.

MUSICIANS waiting. Enter SERVINGMEN with napkins

FIRST SERVINGMAN

Where's Potpan, that he helps not to take away? He
shift a trencher? he scrape a trencher!

SECOND SERVINGMAN

When good manners shall lie all in one or two men's
hands and they unwashed too, 'tis a foul thing.

FIRST SERVINGMAN

Away with the joint-stools, remove the
court-cupboard, look to the plate. Good thou, save
me a piece of marchpane; and, as thou loves me, let
the porter let in Susan Grindstone and Nell.
Anthony, and Potpan!

THIRD SERVINGMAN

Ay, boy, ready.

FIRST SERVINGMAN

You are looked for and called for, asked for and
sought for, in the great chamber.

FOURTH SERVINGMAN

We cannot be here and there too. Cheerly, boys; be
brisk awhile, and the longer liver take all.

Exeunt SERVINGMEN, Enter CAPULET, LADY CAPULET, JULIET, TYBALT, NURSE, and all GUESTS and GENTLEWOMEN to the MASKERS

CAPULET

Welcome, gentlemen! ladies that have their toes
Unplagued with corns will have a bout with you.
Ah ha, my mistresses! which of you all
Will now deny to dance? she that makes dainty,
She, I'll swear, hath corns; am I come near ye now?
Welcome, gentlemen! I have seen the day
That I have worn a visor and could tell
A whispering tale in a fair lady's ear,

Shakespeare often uses language to show character differences. Compare the prose of everyday language of the servants with the blank verse (i.e., poetry) and heightened language of the Capulet noblemen on the next page.

"Potpan": Peter Pan's lesser known flight-challenged younger brother.

The servant's jokes about washing plates (trenchers) and hands provide a contrast to Romeo's solemn speech at the end of Act 1, Scene 4.

Shakespeare repeats the word "for" to emphasize the comical impatience of the first servant.

This form of low comedy was intended for the **groundlings**, who stood in the pit (free of charge), many of whom were servants themselves.

Lord Capulet tries to make light of a painful and often embarrassing condition of women at this time, partial to confining high-heeled dress shoes. Renaissance extreme beauty!

The masks or "visors" worn at the Capulets' party provide an opportunity for Romeo to attend unnoticed - for a while.

Apparently, Lord Capulet fancies himself a foot doctor, match-maker, and party host. A smelly job, any way you look at it.

Such as would please: 'tis gone, 'tis gone, 'tis gone:
You are welcome, gentlemen! come, musicians, play.
A hall, a hall! give room! and foot it, girls.

[Music plays, and they dance.]

More light, you knaves; and turn the tables up,
And quench the fire, the room is grown too hot.
Ah, sirrah, this unlook'd-for sport comes well.
Nay, sit, nay, sit, good cousin Capulet;
For you and I are past our dancing days:
How long is't now since last yourself and I
Were in a mask?

SECOND CAPULET

By'r Lady, thirty years.

CAPULET

What, man! 'tis not so much, 'tis not so much:
'Tis since the nuptial of Lucentio,
Come Pentecost as quickly as it will,
Some five and twenty years; and then we mask'd.

SECOND CAPULET

'Tis more, 'tis more, his son is elder, sir;
His son is thirty.

CAPULET

Will you tell me that?
His son was but a ward two years ago.

ROMEO

[To a Servingman.] What lady's that, which doth
enrich the hand
Of yonder knight?

SERVINGMAN

I know not, sir.

ROMEO

O, she doth teach the torches to burn bright!
It seems she hangs upon the cheek of night
As a rich jewel in an Ethiop's ear;
Beauty too rich for use, for earth too dear!
So shows a snowy dove trooping with crows,
As yonder lady o'er her fellows shows.
The measure done, I'll watch her place of stand,
And, touching hers, make blessed my rude hand.
Did my heart love till now? forswear it, sight!
For I ne'er saw true beauty till this night.

TYBALT

This, by his voice, should be a Montague.
Fetch me my rapier, boy. What dares the slave
Come hither, cover'd with an antic face,
To fleer and scorn at our solemnity?
Now, by the stock and honour of my kin,
To strike him dead, I hold it not a sin.

Capulet's change of topics, from his guests, to his servants, and then to his cousin, indicates the confusion that also allows Romeo to enter unnoticed.

If he knew how long, why did he ask?

Is Lord Capulet hard of hearing or just a pain in the. . . ?

Romeo doth seeth the prettyith Juliet.

Again, Shakespeare uses language to indicate character. The rhyming couplets often mean love is in the air (and Romeo has just taken a deep breath). He's been struck by Cupid's arrow.

Translation: "Yo, BABY!"

Although Tybalt is involved in the violence of this play, his character is one of loyalty and impassioned defense of Juliet and the Capulet family.

CAPULET

Why, how now, kinsman! wherefore storm you so?

TYBALT

Uncle, this is a Montague, our foe,
A villain that is hither come in spite,
To scorn at our solemnity this night.

CAPULET

Young Romeo is it?

TYBALT

'Tis he, that villain Romeo.

CAPULET

Content thee, gentle coz, let him alone;
A bears him like a portly gentleman;
And, to say truth, Verona brags of him
To be a virtuous and well-govern'd youth:
I would not for the wealth of all this town
Here in my house do him disparagement:
Therefore be patient, take no note of him:
It is my will, the which if thou respect,
Show a fair presence and put off these frowns,
An ill-beseeming semblance for a feast.

TYBALT

It fits, when such a villain is a guest:
I'll not endure him.

CAPULET

He shall be endured:
What, goodman boy! I say, he shall: go to;
Am I the master here, or you? go to.
You'll not endure him! God shall mend my soul!
You'll make a mutiny among my guests!
You will set cock-a-hoop! you'll be the man!

TYBALT

Why, uncle, 'tis a shame.

CAPULET

Go to, go to;
You are a saucy boy: is't so, indeed?
This trick may chance to scathe you, I know what:
You must contrary me! marry, 'tis time.
Well said, my hearts! You are a princox; go:
Be quiet, or--More light, more light! For shame!
I'll make you quiet. What, cheerly, my hearts!

TYBALT

Patience perforce with wilful choler meeting
Makes my flesh tremble in their different greeting.
I will withdraw: but this intrusion shall
Now seeming sweet convert to bitt'rest gall.

Exit

Another keen observation, Lord Copulate. . .uh. . .Capulet.

Tybalt's anger is found in his words: "foe," "villain," "spite," and "scorn."

Tybalt has known of Romeo's presence for ten minutes. Welcome to the party, Lord C!

Finally, a rational word from L.C.

Tybalt's threat foreshadows the sword fight between him and Romeo.

His anger in the midst of a happy celebration highlights the theme of love and hate. The love of Romeo and Juliet is set against a background of hatred and family feuds.

Lord Capulet confuses Tybalt for gravy in search of meat.

"princox": impertinent, big-mouth boy.

With Sir Angry-a-lot gone, Romeo makes his move.

ROMEO

[To JULIET.] If I profane with my unworthiest hand
This holy shrine, the gentle sin is this:
My lips, two blushing pilgrims, ready stand
To smooth that rough touch with a tender kiss.

JULIET

Good pilgrim, you do wrong your hand too much,
Which mannerly devotion shows in this;
For saints have hands that pilgrims' hands do touch,
And palm to palm is holy palmers' kiss.

ROMEO

Have not saints lips, and holy palmers too?

JULIET

Ay, pilgrim, lips that they must use in prayer.

ROMEO

O, then, dear saint, let lips do what hands do;
They pray, grant thou, lest faith turn to despair.

JULIET

Saints do not move, though grant for prayers' sake.

ROMEO

Then move not, while my prayer's effect I take.
Thus from my lips, by thine, my sin is purged.

JULIET

Then have my lips the sin that they have took.

ROMEO

Sin from my lips? O trespass sweetly urged!
Give me my sin again.

JULIET

You kiss by the book.

NURSE

Madam, your mother craves a word with you.

ROMEO

What is her mother?

NURSE

Marry, bachelor,
Her mother is the lady of the house,
And a good lady, and a wise and virtuous
I nursed her daughter, that you talk'd withal;
I tell you, he that can lay hold of her
Shall have the chinks.

ROMEO

Is she a Capulet?
O dear account! my life is my foe's debt.

BENVOLIO

Away, be gone; the sport is at the best.

ROMEO

Ay, so I fear; the more is my unrest.

In addition to the religious metaphor used by both young lovers, their language conveys the theme of Romantic Love.

A shift from men treating women as mere objects to seeing them as objects of exalted love. Many critics blame this 12th-century idea of love for Romeo's actions.

Watch his hands, Juliet, watch his hands!

Romeo, the raging hormone.

Romeo's wooing is criticized here by Juliet. She tells Romeo to act naturally, not poetically. This is an important moment in the play, revealing differences in the lovers' character and language.

A woman, we hope.

Translation: "Baby got Bank!"

Here, the play's Exposition gives way to the Rising Action/Problem: Romeo will give his life for Juliet's love.

CAPULET

    Nay, gentlemen, prepare not to be gone;
    We have a trifling foolish banquet towards.
    Is it e'en so? why, then, I thank you all
    I thank you, honest gentlemen; good night.
    More torches here! Come on then, let's to bed.
    Ah, sirrah, by my fay, it waxes late:
    I'll to my rest.

Exeunt all but JULIET and NURSE

JULIET

    Come hither, Nurse. What is yond gentleman?

NURSE

    The son and heir of old Tiberio.

JULIET

    What's he that now is going out of door?

NURSE

    Marry, that, I think, be young Petruchio.

JULIET

    What's he that follows there, that would not dance?

NURSE

    I know not.

JULIET

    Go ask his name: if he be married,
    My grave is like to be my wedding bed.

NURSE

    His name is Romeo, and a Montague;
    The only son of your great enemy.

JULIET

    My only love sprung from my only hate!
    Too early seen unknown, and known too late!
    Prodigious birth of love it is to me,
    That I must love a loathed enemy.

NURSE

    What's this? what's this?

JULIET

    A rhyme I learn'd even now
    Of one I danced withal.

    [One calls within 'Juliet.']

NURSE

    Anon, anon!
    Come, let's away; the strangers all are gone.

Exeunt

We bid farewell to the ever contradictory Lord C. In seven lines he digresses from asking his guests to stay, to announcing that he's going to bed.

"by my fay": By my faith. That is, hey, I speak the truth!

Like Shakespeare's servants, the Nurse offers a comic reprieve from the social and sexual tension created by Romeo's presence at the Capulets' party.

Throughout the play, the Nurse makes bawdy references and sexual puns; however, like King Lear's Fool, she offers sage advice and companionship to Juliet.

Like her cousin Tybalt, Juliet foreshadows the play's climax - must be in the Capulet gene pool.

In addition to Juliet using the rhyming couplet language of love, Shakespeare introduces the theme of intractable fate in the last two lines.

An Elizabethan audience would quickly recognize this and numerous other references to the inevitability of a tragic ending.

Act I Notes

Act I Notes

Act I Notes

Romeo and Juliet
~ Act II, Scene I ~
Scene Synopsis

After the party, Romeo hides from his friends (they make fun of him) and climbs a wall, returning to the Capulet grounds to find Juliet (today, he would be shot or attacked by dogs!).

Prologue

Enter Chorus

CHORUS

Now old desire doth in his deathbed lie,
And young affection gapes to be his heir;
That fair for which love groan'd for and would die,
With tender Juliet match'd, is now not fair.
Now Romeo is beloved and loves again,
Alike betwitched by the charm of looks,
But to his foe supposed he must complain,
And she steal love's sweet bait from fearful hooks:
Being held a foe, he may not have access
To breathe such vows as lovers use to swear;
And she as much in love, her means much less
To meet her new beloved any where:
But passion lends them power, time means, to meet,
Tempering extremities with extreme sweet.

Exit

Scene I
A lane by the wall of Capulet's orchard.

Enter ROMEO

ROMEO

Can I go forward when my heart is here?
Turn back, dull earth, and find thy centre out.

[*He climbs the wall, and leaps down within it* .]

Enter BENVOLIO and MERCUTIO

BENVOLIO

Romeo! my cousin Romeo! Romeo!

MERCUTIO

He is wise;
And, on my life, hath stol'n him home to bed.

BENVOLIO

He ran this way, and leapt this orchard wall:
Call, good Mercutio.

MERCUTIO

Nay, I'll conjure too.
Romeo! humours! madman! passion! lover!
Appear thou in the likeness of a sigh:

"old desire" - Rosaline
"young affection" - Juliet

Notice how the Chorus continues the theme of paradoxes or contrasts: old desire/young affection, deathbed/heir, foe/lover, extremities/extreme sweet.

Hey - they're teens, they'll figure it out.

Romeo uses the metaphor of the "earth" for his body; his heart, its "centre."

Hey Romeo - can you say trespassing? He's in love, give him a break.

Jealousy, thy name is Mercutio.

Speak but one rhyme, and I am satisfied;
Cry but 'Ay me!' pronounce but 'love' and 'dove;'
Speak to my gossip Venus one fair word,
One nickname for her purblind son and heir,
Young Abraham Cupid, he that shot so trim,
When King Cophetua loved the beggar maid!
He heareth not, he stirreth not, he moveth not;
The ape is dead, and I must conjure him.
I conjure thee by Rosaline's bright eyes,
By her high forehead and her scarlet lip,
By her fine foot, straight leg and quivering thigh
And the demesnes that there adjacent lie,
That in thy likeness thou appear to us!

BENVOLIO

And if he hear thee, thou wilt anger him.

MERCUTIO

This cannot anger him: 'twould anger him
To raise a spirit in his mistress' circle
Of some strange nature, letting it there stand
Till she had laid it and conjured it down;
That were some spite: my invocation
Is fair and honest, and in his mistress' name
I conjure only but to raise up him.

BENVOLIO

Come, he hath hid himself among these trees,
To be consorted with the humorous night:
Blind is his love and best befits the dark.

MERCUTIO

If love be blind, love cannot hit the mark.
Now will he sit under a medlar tree,
And wish his mistress were that kind of fruit
As maids call medlars, when they laugh alone.
Romeo, that she were, O, that she were
An open et cetera, and thou a poperin pear!
O Romeo, good night: I'll to my truckle-bed;
This field-bed is too cold for me to sleep:
Come, shall we go?

BENVOLIO

Go, then; for 'tis in vain
To seek him here that means not to be found.

Exeunt

Mercutio alludes to a king who fell in love with the first thing he saw, a poor maid, after being struck by Cupid's arrow.

Shakespeare uses this drug-induced love-at-first-sight in *A Midsummer Night's Dream* as well (a Fairy-Queen falls in love with a man who has the head of a donkey) – no, I'm not kidding!

Mercutio defends mocking Romeo by saying that Romeo would only be mad if he were to insult Rosaline - which subtly, of course, he is.

"consorted": together with, harmonize. Note the negative imagery of love and blindness with darkness.

Again the Cupid theme and love's blindness.

"medlar": a fruit (like a small, brown pear or apple); typically eaten when it falls, almost rotten, from the tree.

"truckle-bed": trundle-bed.

We learn that Romeo does hear Benny because the last line of this scene and Romeo's first line of 2.2 creates a couplet.

Act II, Scene II

Scene Synopsis

In this most famous Shakespearean scene, Romeo overhears Juliet say she loves him (Romeo is, at this point, guilty of trespassing, loitering, and being a peeping Tom!). They play kissy-face briefly, and then arrange to set a time for marriage - yes, that's fast!

Scene II
Capulet's orchard.

Enter ROMEO

ROMEO

He jests at scars that never felt a wound.

[JULIET appears above at a window.]

But, soft! what light through yonder window breaks?
It is the east, and Juliet is the sun.
Arise, fair sun, and kill the envious moon,
Who is already sick and pale with grief,
That thou her maid art far more fair than she:
Be not her maid, since she is envious;
Her vestal livery is but sick and green
And none but fools do wear it; cast it off.
It is my lady, O, it is my love!
O, that she knew she were!
She speaks yet she says nothing: what of that?
Her eye discourses; I will answer it.
I am too bold, 'tis not to me she speaks:
Two of the fairest stars in all the heaven,
Having some business, do entreat her eyes
To twinkle in their spheres till they return.
What if her eyes were there, they in her head?
The brightness of her cheek would shame those stars,
As daylight doth a lamp; her eyes in heaven
Would through the airy region stream so bright
That birds would sing and think it were not night.
See, how she leans her cheek upon her hand!
O, that I were a glove upon that hand,
That I might touch that cheek!

JULIET

Ay me!

ROMEO

She speaks:
O, speak again, bright angel! for thou art
As glorious to this night, being o'er my head
As is a winged messenger of heaven
Unto the white-upturned wondering eyes
Of mortals that fall back to gaze on him
When he bestrides the lazy-pacing clouds
And sails upon the bosom of the air.

This scene contains some of Shakespeare's most beautiful love poetry.

Translation: They make fun of me because they've never been in love.

In one of the play's most famous speeches, Romeo uses celestial imagery to describe Juliet's beauty: sun, moon, stars, and heaven.

Warning:
Guys, I know you're tempted, but don't try these lines on your next date. Remember, Romeo is a trained professional.

25 lines to 1: "Juliet is a hotty!"

Irony: The audience knows Romeo can hear her, but Juliet has no idea that he's there.

In the '96 film, Juliet (Claire Danes) was dressed in an angel costume earlier at the party. The director (Baz Luhrmann) created a visual picture from the textual image. Pretty cool, huh?

JULIET

O Romeo, Romeo! wherefore art thou Romeo?
Deny thy father and refuse thy name;
Or, if thou wilt not, be but sworn my love,
And I'll no longer be a Capulet.

ROMEO

[*Aside.*] Shall I hear more, or shall I speak at this?

JULIET

'Tis but thy name that is my enemy;
Thou art thyself, though not a Montague.
What's Montague? it is nor hand, nor foot,
Nor arm, nor face, nor any other part
Belonging to a man. O, be some other name!
What's in a name? that which we call a rose
By any other word would smell as sweet;
So Romeo would, were he not Romeo call'd,
Retain that dear perfection which he owes
Without that title. Romeo, doff thy name,
And for that name which is no part of thee
Take all myself.

ROMEO

I take thee at thy word:
Call me but love, and I'll be new baptized;
Henceforth I never will be Romeo.

JULIET

What man art thou that thus bescreen'd in night
So stumblest on my counsel?

ROMEO

By a name
I know not how to tell thee who I am:
My name, dear saint, is hateful to myself,
Because it is an enemy to thee;
Had I it written, I would tear the word.

JULIET

My ears have yet not drunk a hundred words
Of thy tongue's uttering, yet I know the sound:
Art thou not Romeo and a Montague?

ROMEO

Neither, fair maid, if either thee dislike.

JULIET

How camest thou hither, tell me, and wherefore?
The orchard walls are high and hard to climb,
And the place death, considering who thou art,
If any of my kinsmen find thee here.

ROMEO

With love's light wings did I o'erperch these walls;
For stony limits cannot hold love out,
And what love can do that dares love attempt;
Therefore thy kinsmen are no stop to me.

Second only to Hamlet's "To be, or not to be," Juliet's line is one of the most quoted and recognized of Shakespeare's works.

To change their names for love? Uh. . . Romeo Smith, this is Juliet Jenkins.

"Aside": spoken to the audience, but no one on stage hears.

Juliet echoes the theme of oppositions begun earlier in the Chorus' opening prologue and by Romeo in 1.1: Montague/not Montague, nor hand/nor foot, etc., Romeo/not Romeo.

"What's in a name": another famous line from the play that deals specifically with loving someone for who they are on the inside, not for a name or money.

"Baptized": The '96 film had Romeo fall into a pool of water.

He doesn't get it – it's the Montague name she's worried about.

Translation: Who 'dat?

Now! Use the Romeo Smith name, now!

From Juliet's response of being able to recognize Romeo's voice we see that he is not the only one hit by Cupid's arrow.

See how she likes Romeo Smith, or Frank Smithino.

Not a phrase the city of Verona would want to use on a travel brochure.

Either Romeo's in love or he's drinking Red Bull™ - whatever, he's got wings.

Tybalt? No problemo!

JULIET

> If they do see thee, they will murder thee.

ROMEO

> Alack, there lies more peril in thine eye
> Than twenty of their swords: look thou but sweet,
> And I am proof against their enmity.

Translation: Love conquers all.

JULIET

> I would not for the world they saw thee here.

ROMEO

> I have night's cloak to hide me from their eyes;
> And but thou love me, let them find me here:
> My life were better ended by their hate,
> Than death prorogued, wanting of thy love.

Again, life/death and love/hate are repeated; Romeo would rather die than be without Juliet's love.

Wasn't he just saying this about Rosaline?

JULIET

> By whose direction found'st thou out this place?

ROMEO

> By love, that first did prompt me to inquire;
> He lent me counsel and I lent him eyes.
> I am no pilot; yet, wert thou as far
> As that vast shore wash'd with the farthest sea,
> I should adventure for such merchandise.

Wow! Romeo has found an all-purpose love, he gets: wings (chicken?), courage, directions, and advice. . .oh yeah, almost forgot – and death, too!

"pilot": sea captain, as explained in the next two lines.

JULIET

> Thou know'st the mask of night is on my face,
> Else would a maiden blush bepaint my cheek
> For that which thou hast heard me speak tonight
> Fain would I dwell on form, fain, fain deny
> What I have spoke: but farewell compliment!
> Dost thou love me? I know thou wilt say 'Ay,'
> And I will take thy word: yet if thou swear'st,
> Thou mayst prove false; at lovers' perjuries
> Then say, Jove laughs. O gentle Romeo,
> If thou dost love, pronounce it faithfully:
> Or if thou think'st I am too quickly won,
> I'll frown and be perverse and say thee nay,
> So thou wilt woo; but else, not for the world.
> In truth, fair Montague, I am too fond,
> And therefore thou mayst think my 'haviour light:
> But trust me, gentleman, I'll prove more true
> Than those that have more cunning to be strange.
> I should have been more strange, I must confess,
> But that thou overheard'st, ere I was ware,
> My true love's passion: therefore pardon me,
> And not impute this yielding to light love,
> Which the dark night hath so discovered.

"fain": gladly.

"think my 'haviour light": don't think I'm easy.

ROMEO

> Lady, by yonder blessed moon I vow
> That tips with silver all these fruit-tree tops--

JULIET

> O, swear not by the moon, th' inconstant moon,

Juliet describes married life.

That monthly changes in her circled orb,
Lest that thy love prove likewise variable.

ROMEO

What shall I swear by?

JULIET

Do not swear at all;
Or, if thou wilt, swear by thy gracious self,
Which is the god of my idolatry,
And I'll believe thee.

ROMEO

If my heart's dear love--

JULIET

Well, do not swear: although I joy in thee,
I have no joy of this contract tonight:
It is too rash, too unadvised, too sudden;
Too like the lightning, which doth cease to be
Ere one can say 'It lightens.' Sweet, good night!
This bud of love, by summer's ripening breath,
May prove a beauteous flower when next we meet.
Good night, good night! as sweet repose and rest
Come to thy heart as that within my breast!

> Translation: "Slow your roll, Romeo!" Juliet is more mature than Romeo and often tries to temper his behavior.

> Given time, our love will grow.

ROMEO

O, wilt thou leave me so unsatisfied?

> Everything is going so well and you have to go *there*!

JULIET

What satisfaction canst thou have tonight?

ROMEO

The exchange of thy love's faithful vow for mine.

> Ah! Nice catch, bring the love thing back into it.

JULIET

I gave thee mine before thou didst request it:
And yet I would it were to give again.

ROMEO

Wouldst thou withdraw it? for what purpose, love?

> Always hearing the negative, she loves you!

JULIET

But to be frank, and give it thee again.
And yet I wish but for the thing I have:
My bounty is as boundless as the sea,
My love as deep; the more I give to thee,
The more I have, for both are infinite.

> See, she likes the name Frank.

> What more could a young man want? Oh yeah, almost forgot – death!

[Nurse calls within.]

I hear some noise within; dear love, adieu!
Anon, good Nurse! Sweet Montague, be true.
Stay but a little, I will come again.

> "adieu": good-bye
> "anon": soon, presently, or used in answering a call.

Exit, above

ROMEO

O blessed, blessed night! I am afeard.
Being in night, all this is but a dream,
Too flattering-sweet to be substantial.

> Romeo alludes to the Elizabethan superstition of the dark and of evil occurrences during the dark of night.

Re-enter JULIET, above

JULIET

Three words, dear Romeo, and good night indeed.
If that thy bent of love be honourable,
Thy purpose marriage, send me word tomorrow,
By one that I'll procure to come to thee,
Where and what time thou wilt perform the rite;
And all my fortunes at thy foot I'll lay
And follow thee my lord throughout the world.

NURSE

[Within.] Madam!

JULIET

I come, anon.--But if thou mean'st not well,
I do beseech thee--

NURSE

[Within.] Madam!

JULIET

By and by, I come:--
To cease thy suit, and leave me to my grief:
Tomorrow will I send.

ROMEO

So thrive my soul--

JULIET

A thousand times good night!

Exit, above

ROMEO

A thousand times the worse, to want thy light.
Love goes toward love, as schoolboys from
their books,
But love from love, toward school with heavy looks.

[Retiring.]

Re-enter JULIET, above

JULIET

Hist! Romeo, hist! O, for a falconer's voice,
To lure this tassel-gentle back again!
Bondage is hoarse, and may not speak aloud;
Else would I tear the cave where Echo lies,
And make her airy tongue more hoarse than mine,
With repetition of my 'Romeo.'

ROMEO

It is my soul that calls upon my name:
How silver-sweet sound lovers' tongues by night,
Like softest music to attending ears!

JULIET

Romeo!

ROMEO

My dear?

JULIET

At what o'clock tomorrow
Shall I send to thee?

"three words": a brief statement. What Juliet says: "What time are we getting married?"

What Romeo should be thinking: "Marriage? Who said anything about. . .look, I know I said 'love,' but all I really wanted was. . . "

Romeo and Juliet are on the balcony outside her room; the Nurse is inside.

"thy suit": Romeo's love for her.

Romeo thinks love feels like the last bell at the end of the school day; being without love feels like the morning walk to your first class.

"falconer": one who trains and works with falcons.

"tassel-gentle": a male falcon.

Juliet wants to call out Romeo's name, but doesn't want anyone else to hear.

"Echo": Greek myth used to explain the reverberation of sound, hence the word "echo."

"silver-sweet sound": alliteration or repetition of the same initial letter; in this case the letter "s."

"o'clock": time (duh!)

ROMEO
By the hour of nine.

JULIET
I will not fail: 'tis twenty years till then.
I have forgot why I did call thee back.

ROMEO
Let me stand here till thou remember it.

JULIET
I shall forget, to have thee still stand there,
Remembering how I love thy company.

ROMEO
And I'll still stay, to have thee still forget,
Forgetting any other home but this.

JULIET
'Tis almost morning; I would have thee gone:
And yet no farther than a wanton's bird;
That lets it hop a little from her hand,
Like a poor prisoner in his twisted gyves,
And with a silk thread plucks it back again,
So loving-jealous of his liberty.

ROMEO
I would I were thy bird.

JULIET
Sweet, so would I:
Yet I should kill thee with much cherishing.
Good night, good night! parting is such
sweet sorrow,
That I shall say good night till it be morrow.

Exit above

ROMEO
Sleep dwell upon thine eyes, peace in thy breast!
Would I were sleep and peace, so sweet to rest!
Hence will I to my ghostly father's cell,
His help to crave, and my dear hap to tell.

Exit

Hmmmm. . .twenty years and she's senile. A lot to look forward to, Romeo.

Whoa, these two have it bad - two bull's-eyes for Cupid!

Like a small pet bird, Juliet wants Romeo to stay close to her.

"gyves": chains, fetters.

"kill thee": foreshadowing of the play's tragic end.
Another infinitely famous line from this scene.

Yeah, "rest" is what he's thinking about.
"ghostly father": a priest, particularly in the confessional.
"hap": good news.

Scene Synopsis

Romeo goes immediately to his priest and friend Friar Laurence (Father Larry) and asks him to marry them that afternoon. Father Larry is a little concerned that MacRomeo is moving too quickly, but agrees in hopes that the marriage will end the gang war between the families - and good luck with all that!

Scene III

Friar Laurence's cell.

Enter FRIAR LAURENCE, with a basket

Shakespeare wrote all of Father Larry's lines in this scene in rhyming couplets.

FRIAR LAURENCE

The grey-eyed morn smiles on the frowning night,
Check'ring the eastern clouds with streaks of light,
And flecked darkness like a drunkard reels
From forth day's path and Titan's fiery wheels:
Now, ere the sun advance his burning eye,
The day to cheer and night's dank dew to dry,
I must up-fill this osier cage of ours
With baleful weeds and precious-juiced flowers.
The earth that's nature's mother is her tomb;
What is her burying grave that is her womb,
And from her womb children of divers kind
We sucking on her natural bosom find,
Many for many virtues excellent,
None but for some and yet all different.
O, mickle is the powerful grace that lies
In plants, herbs, stones, and their true qualities:
For nought so vile that on the earth doth live
But to the earth some special good doth give,
Nor aught so good but strain'd from that fair use
Revolts from true birth, stumbling on abuse:
Virtue itself turns vice, being misapplied;
And vice sometime's by action dignified.
Within the infant rind of this weak flower
Poison hath residence and medicine power:
For this, being smelt, with that part cheers each part;
Being tasted, slays all senses with the heart.
Two such opposed kings encamp them still
In man as well as herbs, grace and rude will;
And where the worser is predominant
Full soon the canker death eats up that plant.

Note the light/dark imagery of the first six lines.

Father Larry explains the similarities between plants and Man: both can be good and/or evil.

Here Father Larry foreshadows the potion he gives Juliet later in the play.

Enter ROMEO

ROMEO

Good morrow, father.

FRIAR LAURENCE

Benedicite!
What early tongue so sweet saluteth me?
Young son, it argues a distemper'd head
So soon to bid good morrow to thy bed:
Care keeps his watch in every old man's eye,

"Benedicite": a priestly "hello."

And where care lodges, sleep will never lie;
But where unbruised youth with unstuff'd brain
Doth couch his limbs, there golden sleep doth reign:
Therefore thy earliness doth me assure
Thou art uproused with some distemperature;
Or if not so, then here I hit it right,
Our Romeo hath not been in bed tonight.

ROMEO

That last is true; the sweeter rest was mine.

FRIAR LAURENCE

God pardon sin! wast thou with Rosaline?

ROMEO

With Rosaline, my ghostly father? no;
I have forgot that name, and that name's woe.

FRIAR LAURENCE

That's my good son: but where hast thou been, then?

ROMEO

I'll tell thee, ere thou ask it me again.
I have been feasting with mine enemy,
Where on a sudden one hath wounded me,
That's by me wounded: both our remedies
Within thy help and holy physic lies:
I bear no hatred, blessed man, for, lo,
My intercession likewise steads my foe.

FRIAR LAURENCE

Be plain, good son, and homely in thy drift;
Riddling confession finds but riddling shrift.

ROMEO

Then plainly know my heart's dear love is set
On the fair daughter of rich Capulet:
As mine on hers, so hers is set on mine;
And all combined, save what thou must combine
By holy marriage: when and where and how
We met, we woo'd and made exchange of vow,
I'll tell thee as we pass; but this I pray,
That thou consent to marry us today.

FRIAR LAURENCE

Holy Saint Francis, what a change is here!
Is Rosaline, that thou didst love so dear,
So soon forsaken? young men's love then lies
Not truly in their hearts, but in their eyes.
Jesu Maria, what a deal of brine
Hath wash'd thy sallow cheeks for Rosaline!
How much salt water thrown away in waste,
To season love, that of it doth not taste!
The sun not yet thy sighs from heaven clears,
Thy old groans ring yet in mine ancient ears;
Lo, here upon thy cheek the stain doth sit
Of an old tear that is not wash'd off yet:

Still rhyming! Maybe this is where Dr. Seuss got the idea.

Translation: There's no way a teenager would be awake this early unless he's been up all night.

F.L. fears Romeo was gettin' jiggy with Rosaline.

Uh, oh, now Romeo's doing it; he responds in rhyme.

Translation: I'm in love with a Capulet (no, not Tybalt!) and I need your help.

"physic": the art of healing diseases; the Renaissance word for medicine.

Come again? Say what?

Romeo 'cuts to the chase.'

Yes, their eyes and elsewhere, good Father.

Father Larry can't believe Romeo has dropped Rosaline so quickly. Shouldn't Juliet consider this as well?!?

If e'er thou wast thyself and these woes thine,
Thou and these woes were all for Rosaline:
And art thou changed? pronounce this sentence then,
Women may fall, when there's no strength in men.

ROMEO

Thou chid'st me oft for loving Rosaline.

"You warned me against loving Rosaline."

FRIAR LAURENCE

For doting, not for loving, pupil mine.

"Well, you were off-into-it."

ROMEO

And bad'st me bury love.

"And you asked me to give it up."

FRIAR LAURENCE

Not in a grave,
To lay one in, another out to have.

Note the love/death metaphor of "grave."

"Not to stop loving one girl just to start loving another."

ROMEO

I pray thee, chide not; she whom I love now
Doth grace for grace and love for love allow;
The other did not so.

"But this girl loves me, too!"

FRIAR LAURENCE

O, she knew well
Thy love did read by rote and could not spell.
But come, young waverer, come, go with me,
In one respect I'll thy assistant be;
For this alliance may so happy prove,
To turn your households' rancour to pure love.

Father Larry has an idea: the marriage of R & J might end this violence between the families.

ROMEO

O, let us hence; I stand on sudden haste.

"I gotta go!"

FRIAR LAURENCE

Wisely and slow; they stumble that run fast.

What is the literal and figurative meaning of the next line?

Exeunt

The '96 film: Romeo trips and falls leaving the church.

∽ Act II, Scene IV ∽

Scene Synopsis

Romeo's homies, Mercutio and Benny, meet-up with him and he is back to his old self again. They see Juliet's Nurse, and Romeo tells her of the plan to get married at Father Larry's church. Romeo sends Juliet the wedding plans via the Nurse, the young lovers' conduit.

Scene IV
A street.

Enter BENVOLIO and MERCUTIO

Recall Mercutio's playful love of language.

MERCUTIO

Where the devil should this Romeo be?
Came he not home tonight?

Watch how Mercutio avoids serious topics through humor and language.

BENVOLIO

Not to his father's; I spoke with his man.

"his man": a servant of the Montagues.

MERCUTIO

Why, that same pale hard-hearted wench, that Rosaline.
Torments him so, that he will sure run mad.

Mercutio does not have a high opinion of love.

BENVOLIO

Tybalt, the kinsman of old Capulet,
Hath sent a letter to his father's house.

MERCUTIO

A challenge, on my life.

BENVOLIO

Romeo will answer it.

MERCUTIO

Any man that can write may answer a letter.

BENVOLIO

Nay, he will answer the letter's master, how he
dares, being dared.

MERCUTIO

Alas poor Romeo! he is already dead; stabbed with a
white wench's black eye; run through the ear with a
love-song; the very pin of his heart cleft with the
blind bow-boy's butt-shaft: and is he a man to
encounter Tybalt?

BENVOLIO

Why, what is Tybalt?

MERCUTIO

More than Prince of Cats, I can tell you. O, he's
the courageous captain of compliments. He fights as
you sing prick-song, keeps time, distance, and
proportion; he rests his minim rests, one, two, and
the third in your bosom: the very butcher of a silk
button, a duellist, a duellist; a gentleman of the
very first house, of the first and second cause:
ah, the immortal *passado*! the *punto reverso*! the
hay!

BENVOLIO

The what?

MERCUTIO

The pox of such antic, lisping, affecting
fantasticoes; these new tuners of accent! 'By Jesu,
a very good blade! a very tall man! a very good
whore!' Why, is not this a lamentable thing,
grandsire, that we should be thus afflicted with
these strange flies, these fashion-mongers, these
pardon-me's, who stand so much on the new form,
that they cannot sit at ease on the old bench? O, their
bones, their bones!

Enter ROMEO

BENVOLIO

Here comes Romeo, here comes Romeo.

MERCUTIO

Without his roe, like a dried herring: O flesh, flesh,
how art thou fishified! Now is he for the numbers

Tybalt likely warns Lord Montague that Romeo should not be seen again around the Capulet home.

It was a matter of personal and family honor for an Elizabethan to respond to a verbal/written challenge or insult.

Mercutio puns on the word "answer": to answer a question or to physically respond to a threat.

Benny believes that lover-boy Romeo can fight, too.

"dead; stabbed": foreshadowing.

Mercutio uses alliteration (repetition of b's) to ask how Romeo, struck w/Cupid's lightest of arrows, can fight a swordsman like Tybalt.

Why does Tybalt think he's all that?

"Prince of Cats": a play on the name Tybert from the epic *Reynard the Fox*.

Mercutio uses a list of dueling (swords) terms: compliments, *passado, reverso*; all puns on similar terms of music and dance.

See, you're not the only one confused by Mercutio's phrases.

Mercutio again plays with the double-meaning of words. He alludes both to people affected by the plague and those who are of the latest fashion in word, manner, and dress.

Mercutio considers Tybalt to be one of these "fashion-mongers."

Mercutio and Benny find Romeo in his usual high spirits and ready for fun with puns.

A boy so nice Benny announces him twice.

that Petrarch flowed in: Laura to his lady was a
kitchen-wench; marry, she had a better love to
berhyme her; Dido a dowdy; Cleopatra a gipsy;
Helen and Hero hildings and harlots; Thisbe a grey
eye or so, but not to the purpose. Signior
Romeo, *bon jour*! there's a French salutation
to your French slop. You gave us the counterfeit
fairly last night.

ROMEO

Good morrow to you both. What counterfeit did I give you?

MERCUTIO

The slip, sir, the slip; can you not conceive?

ROMEO

Pardon, good Mercutio, my business was great; and in
such a case as mine a man may strain courtesy.

MERCUTIO

That's as much as to say, such a case as yours
constrains a man to bow in the hams.

ROMEO

Meaning, to curtsy.

MERCUTIO

Thou hast most kindly hit it.

ROMEO

A most courteous exposition.

MERCUTIO

Nay, I am the very pink of courtesy.

ROMEO

Pink for flower.

MERCUTIO

Right.

ROMEO

Why, then is my pump well flowered.

MERCUTIO

Sure wit: follow me this jest now till thou hast
worn out thy pump, that when the single sole of it
is worn, the jest may remain after the wearing solely singular.

ROMEO

O single-soled jest, solely singular for the
singleness.

MERCUTIO

Come between us, good Benvolio; my wits faint.

ROMEO

Switch and spurs, switch and spurs; or I'll cry a match.

MERCUTIO

Nay, if our wits run the wild-goose chase, I am
done, for thou hast more of the wild goose in one of
thy wits than, I am sure, I have in my whole five:
was I with you there for the goose?

Mercutio alludes to many lovers
from literature and mythology:
numbers- lines of verse.
Petrarch- whose sonnets to
Laura became the very model of
love poetry. Dido- famous tragic
lover of the Greek warrior
Aeneas. Helen of Troy- her
beauty caused the Trojan War.
Hero- whom Leander loved by
Pyramus, comically performed
in *A Midsummer Night's Dream*.

"slip": a piece of counterfeit
money.

"my business": his business is
Juliet.

Mercutio teases Romeo for
being whipped by love.

"pink": paragon or embodiment.

"pump": a light shoe.

Alliteration and puns with "sole"
and "single."

Romeo kills the joke.

Romeo wants to continue the
battle of wits.

"Didn't I score a point with the
'goose' comment?"

ROMEO

Thou wast never with me for anything when thou wast
not there for the goose.

"No, that was lame."

MERCUTIO

I will bite thee by the ear for that jest.

ROMEO

Nay, good goose, bite not.

MERCUTIO

Thy wit is a very bitter sweeting; it is a most
sharp sauce.

"sweeting": a type of apple.

ROMEO

And is it not well served in to a sweet goose?

MERCUTIO

O here's a wit of cheveril, that stretches from an
inch narrow to an ell broad!

"cheveril": flexible.
"broad": obvious to all.

ROMEO

I stretch it out for that word 'broad;' which added
to the goose, proves thee far and wide a broad goose.

MERCUTIO

Why, is not this better now than groaning for love?
now art thou sociable, now art thou Romeo; now art
thou what thou art, by art as well as by nature:
for this drivelling love is like a great natural,
that runs lolling up and down to hide his bauble in a hole.

BENVOLIO

Stop there, stop there.

*Thank you, Benny. Why couldn't
you have spoken up earlier?*

MERCUTIO

Thou desirest me to stop in my tale against the hair.

BENVOLIO

Thou wouldst else have made thy tale large.

MERCUTIO

O, thou art deceived; I would have made it short:
for I was come to the whole depth of my tale; and
meant, indeed, to occupy the argument no longer.

*Yeah, right. Tell that to someone
who hasn't listened to you for
the last act and a half.*

ROMEO

Here's goodly gear!

*Romeo sees the Nurse, a
traditionally large woman, as an
object of sport and ridicule.*

Enter NURSE and PETER

MERCUTIO

A sail, a sail!

*The size of the Nurse's clothing,
in part carried by Peter,
resembles that of a ship.*

BENVOLIO

Two, two; a shirt and a smock.

NURSE

Peter!

PETER

Anon!

NURSE

My fan, Peter.

MERCUTIO

Good Peter, to hide her face; for her fan's the
fairer face.

NURSE

God ye good morrow, gentlemen.

MERCUTIO

God ye good den, fair gentlewoman.

NURSE

Is it good den?

MERCUTIO

'Tis no less, I tell ye, for the bawdy hand of the
dial is now upon the prick of noon.

NURSE

Out upon you! what a man are you!

ROMEO

One, gentlewoman, that God hath made for himself to
mar.

NURSE

By my troth, it is well said; 'for himself to mar,'
quoth a'? Gentlemen, can any of you tell me where I
may find the young Romeo?

ROMEO

I can tell you; but young Romeo will be older when
you have found him than he was when you sought him:
I am the youngest of that name, for fault of a worse.

NURSE

You say well.

MERCUTIO

Yea, is the worst well? very well took, i' faith;
wisely, wisely.

NURSE

If you be he, sir, I desire some confidence with
you.

BENVOLIO

She will indite him to some supper.

MERCUTIO

A bawd, a bawd, a bawd! so ho!

ROMEO

What hast thou found?

MERCUTIO

No hare, sir; unless a hare, sir, in a lenten pie,
that is something stale and hoar ere it be spent.

[*Sings.*]

An old hare hoar,
And an old hare hoar,
Is very good meat in Lent
But a hare that is hoar

Score- Mercutio: 1, Nurse: 0

"morrow": morning.

"good den": late afternoon or
evening.

"bawdy": rude or sexually
suggestive. One of Shakespeare's
most famous sexual images and
a brilliant touch is the "prick of
noon" image.

"mar": to injure or insult.

"By my troth": to speak the truth.

Romeo speaks to the Nurse in
puns to impress and entertain
Mercutio and Benny.

"confidence": private
conversation.

"indite": a highbrow word for
invite; Mercutio's pun on
"bawdy."

Mercutio: 2, Nurse: 0

"hoar": moldy or rotten; again,
Mercutio's pun on "whore."

Songs in Shakespeare's play
constitute a special class of
study and research.

Is too much for a score,
When it hoars ere it be spent.
Romeo, will you come to your father's? We'll
to dinner, thither.

ROMEO

I will follow you.

MERCUTIO

Farewell, ancient lady; farewell,

[*Singing.*]

'lady, lady, lady.'

Exeunt MERCUTIO and BENVOLIO

NURSE

I pray you, sir, what saucy
merchant was this that was so full of his ropery?

ROMEO

A gentleman, nurse, that loves to hear himself talk,
and will speak more in a minute than he will stand
to in a month.

NURSE

An 'a speak anything against me, I'll take him
down, an 'a were lustier than he is, and twenty such
Jacks; and if I cannot, I'll find those that shall.
Scurvy knave! I am none of his flirt-gills; I am
none of his skains-mates. And thou must stand by
too, and suffer every knave to use me at his pleasure?

PETER

I saw no man use you at his pleasure; if I had, my weapon
should quickly have been out, I warrant you: I dare
draw as soon as another man, if I see occasion in a
good quarrel, and the law on my side.

NURSE

Now, afore God, I am so vexed, that every part about
me quivers. Scurvy knave! Pray you, sir, a word:
and as I told you, my young lady bid me inquire you
out; what she bid me say, I will keep to myself.
but first let me tell ye, if ye should lead her into
a fool's paradise, as they say, it were a very gross
kind of behavior, as they say: for the gentlewoman
is young; and, therefore, if you should deal double
with her, truly it were an ill thing to be offered
to any gentlewoman, and very weak dealing.

ROMEO

Nurse, commend me to thy lady and mistress. I
protest unto thee—

NURSE

Good heart, and, i' faith, I will tell her as much:
Lord, Lord, she will be a joyful woman.

Mercutio: 3, Nurse: 0

Mercutio leaves the battle, leading 3 zip over the Nurse. Wait, she takes the offense and rallies.

"saucy": fresh, disrespectful.
"ropery": a knavery, a punishable offense.

There's an understatement.

"Jacks": knaves.
"scurvy": contemptible.
"flirt-gills": loose women.
"skains-mates": underworld cut-throat.

Mercutio: 3, Nurse: 3!

Clearly, Peter was not paying attention. It's always easy to talk trash when the opponent has already left.

Like Mercutio, the Nurse uses twice the number of words required to say something.

Translation: "Be careful with my Juliet!" If she loses her virginity before marriage she's spoiled goods.

ROMEO

What wilt thou tell her, Nurse? Thou dost not mark me.

NURSE

I will tell her, sir, that you do protest; which, as
I take it, is a gentlemanlike offer.

ROMEO

Bid her devise
Some means to come to shrift this afternoon;
And there she shall at Friar Laurence' cell
Be shrived and married. Here is for thy pains.

"shrived": freed from all guilt, in
having confessed one's sins.

Romeo offers the Nurse money.

NURSE

No truly sir; not a penny.

ROMEO

Go to; I say you shall.

"Go to": "Oh, come on now!"

NURSE

This afternoon, sir? well, she shall be there.

ROMEO

And stay, good Nurse, behind the abbey wall:
Within this hour my man shall be with thee
And bring thee cords made like a tackled stair;
Which to the high top-gallant of my joy
Must be my convoy in the secret night.
Farewell; be trusty, and I'll quit thy pains:
Farewell; commend me to thy mistress.

"tackled stair": rope ladder.

NURSE

Now God in heaven bless thee! Hark you, sir.

ROMEO

What say'st thou, my dear Nurse?

NURSE

Is your man secret? Did you ne'er hear say,
Two may keep counsel, putting one away?

ROMEO

I warrant thee, my man's as true as steel.

NURSE

Well, sir; my mistress is the sweetest lady--Lord,
Lord! when 'twas a little prating thing:--O, there
is a nobleman in town, one Paris, that would fain
lay knife aboard; but she, good soul, had as lief
see a toad, a very toad, as see him. I anger her
sometimes and tell her that Paris is the properer
man; but, I'll warrant you, when I say so, she looks
as pale as any clout in the versal world. Doth not
rosemary and Romeo begin both with a letter?

Romeo is told about his
competition, Paris.

"versal": short for "universal."

ROMEO

Ay, Nurse; what of that? Both with an R.

NURSE

Ah, mocker! that's the dog's name. R is for

the--No; I know it begins with some other
letter:--and she hath the prettiest sententious of
it, of you and rosemary, that it would do you good
to hear it.

ROMEO

Commend me to thy lady.

NURSE

Ay, a thousand times.

Exit Romeo

Peter!

An important, though off-
handed, compliment to Romeo
from an older, experienced
woman who appreciates his
potential and goodness.

PETER

Anon!

NURSE

Peter, take my fan, and go before and apace.

Exeunt

∽ Act II, Scene V ∽

Scene Synopsis

The Nurse teases and clowns with Juliet, but finally tells her to meet Romeo, pretending to go to
confession at Father Larry's.

Scene V

Capulet's orchard.

Enter JULIET

JULIET

The clock struck nine when I did send the nurse;
In half an hour she promised to return.
Perchance she cannot meet him: that's not so.
O, she is lame! love's heralds should be thoughts,
Which ten times faster glide than the sun's beams,
Driving back shadows over louring hills:
Therefore do nimble-pinion'd doves draw Love,
And therefore hath the wind-swift Cupid wings.
Now is the sun upon the highmost hill
Of this day's journey, and from nine till twelve
Is three long hours, yet she is not come.
Had she affections and warm youthful blood,
She would be as swift in motion as a ball;
My words would bandy her to my sweet love,
And his to me:
But old folks, many feign as they were dead;
Unwieldy, slow, heavy and pale as lead.
O God, she comes!

Juliet impatiently waits for the
Nurse to return with Romeo's
news of the wedding plans.

"sun/shadows": Juliet continues
the dark/light imagery
associated with love.

"old folks": Juliet also
reintroduces the theme of
young/old and again, in
opposition.

Enter NURSE and PETER

O honey nurse, what news?
Hast thou met with him? Send thy man away.

"honey": sweet, affectionate.

NURSE

> Peter, stay at the gate.

Exit PETER

JULIET

> Now, good sweet nurse,--O Lord, why look'st thou sad?
> Though news be sad, yet tell them merrily;
> If good, thou shamest the music of sweet news
> By playing it to me with so sour a face.

NURSE

> I am aweary, give me leave awhile:
> Fie, how my bones ache! what a jaunce have I had!

JULIET

> I would thou hadst my bones, and I thy news:
> Nay, come, I pray thee, speak; good, good nurse, speak.

NURSE

> Jesu, what haste? can you not stay awhile?
> Do you not see that I am out of breath?

JULIET

> How art thou out of breath, when thou hast breath
> To say to me that thou art out of breath?
> The excuse that thou dost make in this delay
> Is longer than the tale thou dost excuse.
> Is thy news good, or bad? answer to that;
> Say either, and I'll stay the circumstance:
> Let me be satisfied, is't good or bad?

NURSE

> Well, you have made a simple choice; you know not
> how to choose a man: Romeo! no, not he; though his
> face be better than any man's, yet his leg excels
> all men's; and for a hand, and a foot, and a body,
> though they be not to be talked on, yet they are
> past compare: he is not the flower of courtesy,
> but, I'll warrant him, as gentle as a lamb. Go thy
> ways, wench; serve God. What, have you dined at home?

JULIET

> No, no: but all this did I know before.
> What says he of our marriage? What of that?

NURSE

> Lord, how my head aches! what a head have I!
> It beats as it would fall in twenty pieces.
> My back a t' other side,--Ah, my back, my back!
> Beshrew your heart for sending me about,
> To catch my death with jouncing up and down!

JULIET

> I' faith, I am sorry that thou art not well.
> Sweet, sweet, sweet nurse, tell me, what says my love?

Poor Peter. No wonder he's clueless, he's never allowed to hear things.

Paranoia, thy name is Juliet.

The Nurse takes advantage of the opportunity to be the center of Juliet's attention.

"Jesu": The Nurse is a lowly character and naturally swears.

"flower of courtesy": Romeo and Mercutio both made puns on decorated shoes and courtesy/curtsy.

Juliet's patience is running thin.

The old broad is stalling, big time.

"Beshrew": a playful "curse" upon Juliet.

NURSE

Your love says, like an honest gentleman, and a
courteous, and a kind, and a handsome, and, I
warrant, a virtuous,--Where is your mother?

The Nurse teases Juliet with the
news of Romeo; this indicates
the closeness of their bond.

JULIET

Where is my mother! why, she is within;
Where should she be? How oddly thou repliest!
'Your love says, like an honest gentleman,
Where is your mother?'

Yep, she's losing it!

NURSE

O God's lady dear!
Are you so hot? marry, come up, I trow;
Is this the poultice for my aching bones?
Henceforward do your messages yourself.

"marry come up": girl, chill!

"You don't like the way I do it, do
it yourself!"

JULIET

Here's such a coil! come, what says Romeo?

"coil": a to-do, circumstance.

NURSE

Have you got leave to go to shrift to-day?

"shrift": a confessional.

JULIET

I have.

NURSE

Then hie you hence to Friar Laurence' cell;
There stays a husband to make you a wife:
Now comes the wanton blood up in your cheeks,
They'll be in scarlet straight at any news.
Hie you to church; I must another way,
To fetch a ladder, by the which your love
Must climb a bird's nest soon when it is dark:
I am the drudge and toil in your delight,
But you shall bear the burden soon at night.
Go; I'll to dinner: hie you to the cell.

Finally, Juliet is to meet Romeo
tonight to get married.

JULIET

Hie to high fortune! Honest nurse, farewell.

Exeunt

Our playwright achieves both low
humor and high suspense in this
short, but important, scene.

⁓ Act II, Scene VI ⁓

Scene Synopsis

Romeo marries Juliet in a short-and-sweet ceremony.

Scene VI

Friar Laurence's cell.

Enter FRIAR LAURENCE and ROMEO

FRIAR LAURENCE

So smile the heavens upon this holy act,
That after hours with sorrow chide us not!

Father Larry must not be feeling
well—he's out of rhymes. Note the
theme of oppositions:
smile/sorrow.

ROMEO

Amen, amen! but come what sorrow can,
It cannot countervail the exchange of joy
That one short minute gives me in her sight:
Do thou but close our hands with holy words,
Then love-devouring death do what he dare;
It is enough I may but call her mine.

FRIAR LAURENCE

These violent delights have violent ends
And in their triumph die, like fire and powder,
Which as they kiss consume: the sweetest honey
Is loathsome in his own deliciousness
And in the taste confounds the appetite:
Therefore love moderately; long love doth so;
Too swift arrives as tardy as too slow.

Enter JULIET

Here comes the lady: O, so light a foot
Will ne'er wear out the everlasting flint:
A lover may bestride the gossamer
That idles in the wanton summer air,
And yet not fall; so light is vanity.

JULIET

Good even to my ghostly confessor.

FRIAR LAURENCE

Romeo shall thank thee, daughter, for us both.

JULIET

As much to him, else is his thanks too much.

ROMEO

Ah, Juliet, if the measure of thy joy
Be heap'd like mine and that thy skill be more
To blazon it, then sweeten with thy breath
This neighbour air, and let rich music's tongue
Unfold the imagined happiness that both
Receive in either by this dear encounter.

JULIET

Conceit, more rich in matter than in words,
Brags of his substance, not of ornament:
They are but beggars that can count their worth;
But my true love is grown to such excess
I cannot sum up sum of half my wealth.

FRIAR LAURENCE

Come, come with me, and we will make short work;
For, by your leaves, you shall not stay alone
Till holy church incorporate two in one.

Exeunt

That's it, Romeo. It's always good to talk of death at your own wedding.

In this pivotal scene, Shakespeare emphasizes themes: violent delights/violent ends, sweetest/loathsome, swift/tardy.

"True love takes time."

After Father Larry's speech, until he sees Juliet. I wonder if he's using a little of the herb himself.

"gossamer": cobweb, often used to describe fairies' wings, like Mercutio's Queen Mab.

All three characters are nervously exchanging hellos.

Right back atcha!

Contrasting images: the '68 film showed R & J kneeling, facing the priest, as they took their wedding vows. The '96 film revealed R & J looking into one another's eyes. A difference in time period or religious emphasis?

"Conceit": understanding.

Okay, kids, let's do this!

Act II Notes

Act II Notes

Act II Notes

Romeo and Juliet
～ Act III, Scene I ～
Scene Synopsis

The play's crisis or turning-point. Here's what happens: Tybalt starts a fight with the ever-insulting Mercutio; Romeo tries to intercede; Mercutio is killed. Romeo takes revenge on Tybalt; Tybalt is killed. The Capulets want Romeo's head; the ever-frustrated Prince banishes Romeo from Verona. After the events of Act 3.1, the lives of all the characters are forever changed. The climax of the play, usually found in the middle of classical tragedy, does not occur until Act 5. Shakespeare became known as a "rebel" for breaking the conventions or rules of dramatic structure. *Go Will! Go Will!*

Scene I
A public place.

Enter MERCUTIO, BENVOLIO, PAGE, and SERVANTS

BENVOLIO

    I pray thee, good Mercutio, let's retire:
    The day is hot, the Capulets abroad,
    And, if we meet, we shall not scape a brawl;
    For now, these hot days, is the mad blood stirring.

MERCUTIO

    Thou art like one of those fellows that when he
    enters the confines of a tavern claps me his sword
    upon the table and says 'God send me no need of
    thee!' and by the operation of the second cup draws
    him on the drawer, when indeed there is no need.

BENVOLIO

    Am I like such a fellow?

MERCUTIO

    Come, come, thou art as hot a Jack in thy mood as
    any in Italy, and as soon moved to be moody, and as
    soon moody to be moved.

BENVOLIO

    And what to?

MERCUTIO

    Nay, an there were two such, we should have none
    shortly, for one would kill the other. Thou! why,
    thou wilt quarrel with a man that hath a hair more,
    or a hair less, in his beard, than thou hast: thou
    wilt quarrel with a man for cracking nuts, having no
    other reason but because thou hast hazel eyes: what
    eye but such an eye would spy out such a quarrel?
    Thy head is as full of quarrels as an egg is full of
    meat, and yet thy head hath been beaten as addle as
    an egg for quarrelling: thou hast quarrelled with a
    man for coughing in the street, because he hath
    wakened thy dog that hath lain asleep in the sun:
    didst thou not fall out with a tailor for wearing
    his new doublet before Easter? with another, for

Side notes:

Even the place foreshadows trouble; the last fight (Act I) was also in a public place.

A Page was a personal servant, used for errands and messages.

Benny forewarns Mercutio of trouble: tension between the families (if they only knew!) and the weather: "hot," "brawl," "hot," "mad blood."

Mercutio compares Benny to a man who is ready to fight by the second drink. Wordplay: "Draw(er)": a waiter; to pour a drink; to brandish a sword.

Mercutio's language reveals his playful mood, despite Benny's cautions. Note how Shakespeare has switched from formal verse with Mercutio to common prose.

"Who me????????"

"mood/moody/moved": temper, quick to anger and note the alliteration (the "m's").

Mercutio pretends to misunderstand Benny, making his "to": "two."

Irony of ironies: After joking with Benny about quarreling (which he most assuredly is not), Mercutio starts an argument with Tybalt.

"doublet": a tight-fitting jacket.

tying his new shoes with old riband? and yet thou
wilt tutor me from quarrelling!

BENVOLIO

An I were so apt to quarrel as thou art, any man
should buy the fee simple of my life for an hour and a quarter.

MERCUTIO

The fee simple! O simple!

BENVOLIO

By my head, here come the Capulets.

MERCUTIO

By my heel, I care not.

Enter TYBALT and others

TYBALT

Follow me close, for I will speak to them.
Gentlemen, good den: a word with one of you.

MERCUTIO

And but one word with one of us? couple it with
something; make it a word and a blow.

TYBALT

You shall find me apt enough to that, sir, an you
will give me occasion.

MERCUTIO

Could you not take some occasion without giving?

TYBALT

Mercutio, thou consort'st with Romeo,--

MERCUTIO

Consort! what, dost thou make us minstrels? an
thou make minstrels of us, look to hear nothing but
discords: here's my fiddlestick; here's that shall
make you dance. 'Zounds, consort!

BENVOLIO

We talk here in the public haunt of men:
Either withdraw unto some private place,
Or reason coldly of your grievances,
Or else depart; here all eyes gaze on us.

MERCUTIO

Men's eyes were made to look, and let them gaze;
I will not budge for no man's pleasure, I.

Enter ROMEO

TYBALT

Well, peace be with you, sir: here comes my man.

MERCUTIO

But I'll be hanged, sir, if he wear your livery:
Marry, go before to field, he'll be your follower;
Your worship in that sense may call him 'man.'

"riband": ribbon.

Translation: "Yeah, and if I were a
hot-head like you, my life
wouldn't be worth much."

"Quit trippin'- we're 'bout to
throwdown."

Mercutio the player, meet Tybalt
the hater.

Mercutio taunts Tybalt with
(seemingly) playful remarks.

"an": if. Sometimes used for
"and," too.

Playah Hatah!

Again, Mercutio's wordplay; a pun
on "consort": to relate with; a
group of musicians.

"fiddlestick": sword.
"Zounds": God's wounds. A
sacred oath and form of swearing.

"Either take this outside (oh,
we're already outside) or forget it;
everyone is watching."

"Let 'em look. If we bounce, we
bounce."

"my man": a common term for a
servant. Tybalt means "who I'm
looking for."

"livery": a servant's uniform.

TYBALT

Romeo, the love I bear thee can afford
No better term than this,—thou art a villain.

ROMEO

Tybalt, the reason that I have to love thee
Doth much excuse the appertaining rage
To such a greeting: villain am I none;
Therefore farewell; I see thou know'st me not.

TYBALT

Boy, this shall not excuse the injuries
That thou hast done me; therefore turn and draw.

ROMEO

I do protest, I never injured thee,
But love thee better than thou canst devise,
Till thou shalt know the reason of my love:
And so, good Capulet,—which name I tender
As dearly as mine own,—be satisfied.

MERCUTIO

O calm, dishonourable, vile submission!
Alla stoccata carries it away.

[*Draws.*]

Tybalt, you rat-catcher, will you walk?

TYBALT

What wouldst thou have with me?

MERCUTIO

Good King of Cats, nothing but one of your nine
lives; that I mean to make bold withal, and as you
shall use me hereafter, drybeat the rest of the
eight. Will you pluck your sword out of his pilcher
by the ears? make haste, lest mine be about your
ears ere it be out.

TYBALT

I am for you.

[*Drawing.*]

ROMEO

Gentle Mercutio, put thy rapier up.

MERCUTIO

Come, sir, your *passado*.

[*They fight.*]

ROMEO

Draw, Benvolio; beat down their weapons.
Gentlemen, for shame, forbear this outrage!
Tybalt, Mercutio, the Prince expressly hath
Forbid bandying in Verona streets:
Hold, Tybalt! good Mercutio!

*TYBALT under ROMEO's arm stabs MERCUTIO, and flies with
his followers*

"villain": a person of low status and a scoundrel.

Translation: "Uh, don't hate - I just married your cousin. Tybalt - we're related!"

Tybalt is not challenging Romeo to a sketching contest - he's ready to fight.

Romeo tries to calm Tybalt: "love," "good Capulet," and "dearly."

"tender": carry or keep, hold.

"*Alla stoccata*": a fencing term for "with the thrust." Mercutio refers to Tybalt's challenge.

"rat-catcher": an allusion to the earlier "Prince of Cats."

He may fight well, but he's a little slow on the uptake.

"drybeat": after taking one of your nine lives, I may only need to whip the other eight.

"BRING-IT-ON!!!!!" You have me as a fighting partner.

Romeo - he's a player, not a fighter. "rapier": two-edged sword.

"*passado*": a fencing term; a thrust, with one foot advanced.

Translation: "We're gonna step into it now!"

MERCUTIO

    I am hurt.
    A plague o' both your houses! I am sped. Is he gone, and
    hath nothing?

A curse on the Montagues and Capulets.

He took nothing but your life.

BENVOLIO

    What, art thou hurt?

That Benny - nothing gets past him: he sees Tybalt stab him and yet he has to ask.

MERCUTIO

    Ay, ay, a scratch, a scratch; marry, 'tis enough.
    Where is my page? Go, villain, fetch a surgeon.

Exit PAGE

ROMEO

    Courage, man; the hurt cannot be much.

Sure, easy for you to say!

MERCUTIO

    No, 'tis not so deep as a well, nor so wide as a
    church door; but 'tis enough,'twill serve: ask for
    me tomorrow, and you shall find me a grave man. I
    am peppered, I warrant, for this world. A plague o'
    both your houses! 'Zounds, a dog, a rat, a mouse, a
    cat, to scratch a man to death! a braggart, a
    rogue, a villain, that fights by the book of
    arithmetic! Why the devil came you between us? I
    was hurt under your arm.

Even while dying, Mercutio is ever "the mouth" of the play; he still has time for a pun: "grave": sadness; a place of burial.

Mercutio alludes to Romeo, who blocks his vision to keep Mercutio from seeing Tybalt's sword.

ROMEO

    I thought all for the best.

Hah! Look what your thinking got me!

MERCUTIO

    Help me into some house, Benvolio,
    Or I shall faint. A plague o' both your houses!
    They have made worms' meat of me: I have it,
    And soundly too: your houses!

So Benny is just supposed to pick ANY house? What if no one's home? What if they have dogs? What then? This is "suspension of disbelief" – big time!

Exeunt MERCUTIO and BENVOLIO

ROMEO

    This gentleman, the Prince's near ally,
    My very friend, hath got his mortal hurt
    In my behalf; my reputation stain'd
    With Tybalt's slander,--Tybalt, that an hour
    Hath been my cousin! O sweet Juliet,
    Thy beauty hath made me effeminate
    And in my temper soften'd valour's steel!

After the fact, Romeo, after the fact.

Juliet has turned Romeo into a girly-man. (No, he doesn't wear a dress, he just wants to use his testosterone differently.)

Re-enter BENVOLIO

BENVOLIO

    O Romeo, Romeo, brave Mercutio's dead!
    That gallant spirit hath aspired the clouds,
    Which too untimely here did scorn the earth.

Benny speaks of Mercutio's spirit ascending (there's an assumption!).

ROMEO

    This day's black fate on more days doth depend;
    This but begins the woe, others must end.

Translation: "Tybalt started it, I'm going to finish it."

BENVOLIO

    Here comes the furious Tybalt back again.

ROMEO

Alive, in triumph! and Mercutio slain!
Away to heaven, respective lenity,
And fire-eyed fury be my conduct now!

Re-enter TYBALT

Now, Tybalt, take the villain back again,
That late thou gavest me; for Mercutio's soul
Is but a little way above our heads,
Staying for thine to keep him company:
Either thou, or I, or both, must go with him.

Advice to Tybalt; Don't hate the player, hate the game.

"Cloud 9 leaving for heaven, first stop The Pearly Gates, one seat available, All Aboard!"

TYBALT

Thou, wretched boy, that didst consort him here,
Shalt with him hence.

ROMEO

This shall determine that.

[They fight; TYBALT falls.]

Romeo gives Tybalt a seat on Cloud 9.

BENVOLIO

Romeo, away, be gone!
The citizens are up, and Tybalt slain.
Stand not amazed: the Prince will doom thee death,
If thou art taken: hence, be gone, away!

"Dude, RUN!"

ROMEO

O, I am fortune's fool!

Wasn't he "fortune's fool" when he got married?

BENVOLIO

Why dost thou stay?

Exit ROMEO

Enter CITIZENS

FIRST CITIZEN

Which way ran he that kill'd Mercutio?
Tybalt, that murderer, which way ran he?

BENVOLIO

There lies that Tybalt.

Apparently, he didn't run far.

FIRST CITIZEN

Up, sir, go with me;
I charge thee in the Prince's name, obey.

Enter PRINCE, attended; MONTAGUE, CAPULET, their WIVES, and others

PRINCE

Where are the vile beginners of this fray?

BENVOLIO

O noble Prince, I can discover all
The unlucky manage of this fatal brawl:
There lies the man, slain by young Romeo,
That slew thy kinsman, brave Mercutio.

Leave it to Benny to break into rhyming couplets when describing the fight.

LADY CAPULET

Tybalt, my cousin! O my brother's child!
O Prince! husband! O, the blood is spilled

Just a guess: she might be upset.

Of my dear kinsman! Prince, as thou art true,
For blood of ours, shed blood of Montague.
O cousin, cousin!

PRINCE

Benvolio, who began this bloody fray?

BENVOLIO

Tybalt, here slain, whom Romeo's hand did slay;   Benny spills the beans.
Romeo that spoke him fair, bid him bethink
How nice the quarrel was, and urged withal
Your high displeasure: all this uttered
With gentle breath, calm look, knees humbly bow'd,
Could not take truce with the unruly spleen
Of Tybalt deaf to peace, but that he tilts
With piercing steel at bold Mercutio's breast,
Who all as hot, turns deadly point to point,
And, with a martial scorn, with one hand beats
Cold death aside, and with the other sends
It back to Tybalt, whose dexterity,
Retorts it: Romeo he cries aloud,
'Hold, friends! friends, part!' and, swifter than
his tongue,
His agile arm beats down their fatal points,
And 'twixt them rushes; underneath whose arm
An envious thrust from Tybalt hit the life
Of stout Mercutio, and then Tybalt fled;
But by and by comes back to Romeo,
Who had but newly entertain'd revenge,
And to 't they go like lightning, for, ere I
Could draw to part them, was stout Tybalt slain.   (Coward!)
And, as he fell, did Romeo turn and fly.
This is the truth, or let Benvolio die.

LADY CAPULET

He is a kinsman to the Montague;   Translation: "You're a liar."
Affection makes him false; he speaks not true:
Some twenty of them fought in this black strife,
And all those twenty could but kill one life.
I beg for justice, which thou, Prince, must give;
Romeo slew Tybalt, Romeo must not live.

PRINCE

Romeo slew him, he slew Mercutio;   Hmmmmm. . . looks like a tie.
Who now the price of his dear blood doth owe?   Overtime, anyone?

MONTAGUE

Not Romeo, Prince, he was Mercutio's friend;
His fault concludes but what the law should end,
The life of Tybalt.

PRINCE

And for that offense   Romeo is banished from Verona.
Immediately we do exile him hence: (You know the Prince is serious
I have an interest in your hate's proceeding,   when he rhymes.)
My blood for your rude brawls doth lie a-bleeding;

But I'll amerce you with so strong a fine
That you shall all repent the loss of mine:
I will be deaf to pleading and excuses;
Nor tears nor prayers shall purchase out abuses:
Therefore use none: let Romeo hence in haste,
Else, when he is found, that hour is his last.
Bear hence this body and attend our will:
Mercy but murders, pardoning those that kill.

Exeunt

"amerce you": punish you.

Prince Busta-Rhymes

❧ Act III, Scene II ❧

Scene Synopsis

The Nurse tells Juliet of Tybalt's death (in her own diesel-truck, delicate manner) and promises to arrange for R & J to have a wedding night (get their freak-on) before Romeo leaves town.

Scene II
Capulet's orchard.

Enter JULIET

JULIET

Gallop apace, you fiery-footed steeds,
Towards Phoebus' lodging: such a wagoner
As Phaethon would whip you to the west,
And bring in cloudy night immediately.
Spread thy close curtain, love-performing night,
That runaway's eyes may wink and Romeo
Leap to these arms, untalk'd of and unseen.
Lovers can see to do their amorous rites
By their own beauties; or, if love be blind,
It best agrees with night. Come, civil night,
Thou sober-suited matron, all in black,
And learn me how to lose a winning match,
Play'd for a pair of stainless maidenhoods:
Hood my unmann'd blood, bating in my cheeks,
With thy black mantle; till strange love, grown bold,
Think true love acted simple modesty.
Come, night; come, Romeo; come, thou day in night;
For thou wilt lie upon the wings of night
Whiter than new snow on a raven's back.
Come, gentle night, come, loving, black-brow'd night,
Give me my Romeo; and, when he shall die,
Take him and cut him out in little stars,
And he will make the face of heaven so fine
That all the world will be in love with night
And pay no worship to the garish sun.
O, I have bought the mansion of a love,
But not possess'd it, and, though I am sold,
Not yet enjoy'd: so tedious is this day
As is the night before some festival
To an impatient child that hath new robes
And may not wear them. O, here comes my Nurse,

Juliet: "Romeo, rock my world!"

Phoebus: Sun God.

Phaethon: Phoebus' son, who loses control of the horses pulling the chariot.

"runaway's eyes": This image's meaning has become controversial. The Folger Library notes that the Variorum edition of this play has twenty-nine pages on whether the phrase is "rundaway eyes," "runaway's eyes," or "runaways' eyes." Early editions of the play are inconsistent. The image must refer to Romeo, a runaway lover, presently out of sight.

Note the repetition of "night," "black," and the foreshadowing of death/marriage. Again, the opposite images support this continuing theme.

"When he shall die," etc. These beautiful poetic lines were spoken by Senator Teddy Kennedy at JFK's funeral mass.

Shakespeare shows us the impatient Juliet waiting for her lover, Romeo. This soliloquy begins the scene in an upbeat way before the bad news of Tybalt's death and Romeo's banishment.

And she brings news; and every tongue that speaks
But Romeo's name speaks heavenly eloquence.

Enter NURSE, with cords

"the cords": the rope ladder for Romeo to use.

Now, Nurse, what news? What hast thou there? the cords
That Romeo bid thee fetch?

NURSE

Ay, ay, the cords.

[Throws them down.]

JULIET

Ay me! what news? why dost thou wring thy hands?

"What is wrong with you?"

NURSE

Ah, well-a-day! he's dead, he's dead, he's dead!
We are undone, lady, we are undone!
Alack the day! he's gone, he's kill'd, he's dead!

Juliet thinks the Nurse is talking about Romeo. Yes, this is foreshadowing and a dramatic instance of tremendous miscommunication, a theme of the play.

JULIET

Can heaven be so envious?

NURSE

Romeo can,
Though heaven cannot: O Romeo, Romeo!
Who ever would have thought it? Romeo!

Recall from Act II how the Nurse has a difficult time getting to the point.

JULIET

What devil art thou, that dost torment me thus?
This torture should be roar'd in dismal hell.
Hath Romeo slain himself? say thou but 'I,'
And that bare vowel 'I' shall poison more
Than the death-darting eye of cockatrice:
I am not I, if there be such an I;
Or those eyes shut, that makes thee answer 'I.'
If he be slain, say 'I'; or if not, no:
Brief sounds determine of my weal or woe.

Juliet, in her confusion and fear, plays with the Elizabethan word for yes, "ay," which creates a pun with "I" and "eye."

"cockatrice": a mythical bird (or serpent, in some sources) which could kill with one glance.

NURSE

I saw the wound, I saw it with mine eyes,--
God save the mark!--here on his manly breast:
A piteous corse, a bloody piteous corse;
Pale, pale as ashes, all bedaub'd in blood,
All in gore-blood; I swounded at the sight.

Notice that Nursey still hasn't told her WHO is dead!

JULIET

O, break, my heart! poor bankrupt, break at once!
To prison, eyes, ne'er look on liberty!
Vile earth, to earth resign; end motion here;
And thou and Romeo press one heavy bier!

Foreshadowing of the tomb where Juliet will be placed.

NURSE

O Tybalt, Tybalt, the best friend I had!
O courteous Tybalt! honest gentleman!
That ever I should live to see thee dead!

JULIET

What storm is this that blows so contrary?
Is Romeo slaughter'd, and is Tybalt dead?

My dearest cousin, and my dearer lord?
Then, dreadful trumpet, sound the general doom!
For who is living, if those two are gone?

NURSE

Tybalt is gone, and Romeo banished;
Romeo that kill'd him, he is banished.

Finally! Way to be brief, Nurse.

JULIET

O God! did Romeo's hand shed Tybalt's blood?

NURSE

It did, it did; alas the day, it did!

JULIET

O serpent heart, hid with a flowering face!
Did ever dragon keep so fair a cave?
Beautiful tyrant! fiend angelical!
Dove-feather'd raven! wolvish-ravening lamb!
Despised substance of divinest show!
Just opposite to what thou justly seem'st,
A damned saint, an honourable villain!
O nature, what hadst thou to do in hell,
When thou didst bower the spirit of a fiend
In mortal paradise of such sweet flesh?
Was ever book containing such vile matter
So fairly bound? O that deceit should dwell
In such a gorgeous palace!

Okay, as if you haven't caught
on already! Notice the opposite
images that Juliet uses: serpent
heart/flowering face, dragon/fair
cave, beautiful/tyrant,
fiend/angelic, etc.

NURSE

There's no trust,
No faith, no honesty in men; all perjured,
All forsworn, all naught, all dissemblers.
Ah, where's my man? give me some *aqua vitae*:
These griefs, these woes, these sorrows make me old.
Shame come to Romeo!

Translation: Careful, young miss,
boys will lie.

JULIET

Blister'd be thy tongue
For such a wish! he was not born to shame:
Upon his brow shame is ashamed to sit;
For 'tis a throne where honour may be crown'd
Sole monarch of the universal earth.
O, what a beast was I to chide at him!

She's changed her mind
already!

NURSE

Will you speak well of him that kill'd your cousin?

JULIET

Shall I speak ill of him that is my husband?
Ah, poor my lord, what tongue shall smooth thy name,
When I, thy three-hours wife, have mangled it?
But, wherefore, villain, didst thou kill my cousin?
That villain cousin would have kill'd my husband:
Back, foolish tears, back to your native spring;
Your tributary drops belong to woe,
Which you, mistaking, offer up to joy.
My husband lives, that Tybalt would have slain;

Juliet doth reason correctly:
if Romeo had not killed him,
Tybalt would have killed Romeo.

And Tybalt's dead, that would have slain my husband:
All this is comfort; wherefore weep I then?
Some word there was, worser than Tybalt's death,
That murder'd me: I would forget it fain;
But, O, it presses to my memory,
Like damned guilty deeds to sinners' minds:
'Tybalt is dead, and Romeo--banished;'
That 'banished,' that one word 'banished,'
Hath slain ten thousand Tybalts. Tybalt's death
Was woe enough, if it had ended there:
Or, if sour woe delights in fellowship
And needly will be rank'd with other griefs,
Why follow'd not, when she said 'Tybalt's dead,'
Thy father, or thy mother, nay, or both,
Which modern lamentation might have moved?
But with a rearward following Tybalt's death,
'Romeo is banished,' to speak that word,
Is father, mother, Tybalt, Romeo, Juliet,
All slain, all dead. 'Romeo is banished!'
There is no end, no limit, measure, bound,
In that word's death; no words can that woe sound.
Where is my father, and my mother, Nurse?

In this line, "banished" is pronounced "ban-eh-shed" - three syllables to make the ten-beat iambic pentameter. It also rhymes with "dead."

NURSE

Weeping and wailing over Tybalt's corse:
Will you go to them? I will bring you thither.

"corse": or corpse, a dead body.

JULIET

Wash they his wounds with tears: mine shall be spent,
When theirs are dry, for Romeo's banishment.
Take up those cords: poor ropes, you are beguiled,
Both you and I; for Romeo is exiled:
He made you for a highway to my bed;
But I, a maid, die maiden-widowed.
Come, cords, come, Nurse; I'll to my wedding bed;
And death, not Romeo, take my maidenhead!

Somebody's just a little preoccupied with herself, now, aren't we? (Don't you hate it when your parents say that!)

NURSE

Hie to your chamber: I'll find Romeo
To comfort you: I wot well where he is.
Hark ye, your Romeo will be here at night:
I'll to him; he is hid at Laurence' cell.

"Wot": know.

JULIET

O, find him! give this ring to my true knight,
And bid him come to take his last farewell.

Well, it's a short marriage - but a happy one - well, sort-of.

Exeunt

Act III, Scene III

Scene Synopsis

Now Romeo is told the bad news: he must leave Verona and be separated from his woman. Father Larry and the Nurse send Romeo to be with Juliet. While he is living in Mantua, Larry sends him a letter through his man, Balthasar.

Scene III

Friar Laurence's cell.

Enter FRIAR LAURENCE

FRIAR LAURENCE

Romeo, come forth; come forth, thou fearful man:
Affliction is enamour'd of thy parts,
And thou art wedded to calamity.

Not the best way to cheer someone up.

Enter ROMEO

ROMEO

Father, what news? what is the Prince's doom?
What sorrow craves acquaintance at my hand,
That I yet know not?

FRIAR LAURENCE

Too familiar
Is my dear son with such sour company:
I bring thee tidings of the Prince's doom.

What is up with the Nurse and Father Larry? Say it, already!

ROMEO

What less than doomsday is the Prince's doom?

"Is he going to kill me or not?!"

FRIAR LAURENCE

A gentler judgement vanish'd from his lips,
Not body's death, but body's banishment.

"vanish'd": issued.
"vanish'd/banishment" - Dr. Seuss has nothin' on Father Larry.

ROMEO

Ha, banishment! be merciful, say 'death;'
For exile hath more terror in his look,
Much more than death: do not say 'banishment.'

Death would be better than being without Juliet. (Hey, what about Rosaline!?!)

FRIAR LAURENCE

Hence from Verona art thou banished:
Be patient, for the world is broad and wide.

ROMEO

There is no world without Verona walls,
But purgatory, torture, hell itself.
Hence-banished is banish'd from the world,
And world's exile is death: then banished,
Is death misterm'd: calling death banishment,
Thou cut'st my head off with a golden axe,
And smilest upon the stroke that murders me.

He's not taking this well at all.

FRIAR LAURENCE

O deadly sin! O rude unthankfulness!
Thy fault our law calls death; but the kind Prince,
Taking thy part, hath rush'd aside the law,

We know he's mad when Father Larry forgets to rhyme.

And turn'd that black word death to banishment:
This is dear mercy, and thou seest it not.

ROMEO

'Tis torture, and not mercy: heaven is here,
Where Juliet lives; and every cat and dog
And little mouse, every unworthy thing,
Live here in heaven and may look on her;
But Romeo may not: more validity,
More honourable state, more courtship lives
In carrion flies than Romeo: they may seize
On the white wonder of dear Juliet's hand
And steal immortal blessing from her lips,
Who even in pure and vestal modesty,
Still blush, as thinking their own kisses sin;
But Romeo may not; he is banished:
Flies may do this, but I from this must fly:
They are free men, but I am banished.
And say'st thou yet that exile is not death?
Hadst thou no poison mix'd, no sharp-ground knife,
No sudden mean of death, though ne'er so mean,
But 'banished' to kill me?--'banished'?
O Friar, the damned use that word in hell;
Howling attends it: how hast thou the heart,
Being a divine, a ghostly confessor,
A sin-absolver, and my friend profess'd,
To mangle me with that word 'banished'?

FRIAR LAURENCE

Thou fond mad man, hear me a little speak.

ROMEO

O, thou wilt speak again of banishment.

FRIAR LAURENCE

I'll give thee armour to keep off that word:
Adversity's sweet milk, philosophy,
To comfort thee, though thou art banished.

ROMEO

Yet 'banished'? Hang up philosophy!
Unless philosophy can make a Juliet,
Displant a town, reverse a Prince's doom,
It helps not, it prevails not: talk no more.

FRIAR LAURENCE

O, then I see that madmen have no ears.

ROMEO

How should they, when that wise men have no eyes?

FRIAR LAURENCE

Let me dispute with thee of thy estate.

ROMEO

Thou canst not speak of that thou dost not feel:
Wert thou as young as I, Juliet thy love,
An hour but married, Tybalt murdered,

Hey, Romeo! Animals are people, too!

"validity": worth.

Hey, Romeo! Father Larry didn't say it, the Prince did!

Welcome to the attitudinal, Romeo.

Romeo turns a deaf ear to reason.

"You don't understand!"

"estate": current condition.

Romeo says, "Unless you're me, you don't understand."

Doting like me and like me banished,
Then mightst thou speak, then mightst thou tear thy hair,
And fall upon the ground, as I do now,
Taking the measure of an unmade grave.

"grave": foreshadowing.

[Knocking within.]

FRIAR LAURENCE

Arise; one knocks; good Romeo, hide thyself.

ROMEO

Not I; unless the breath of heartsick groans,
Mist-like, infold me from the search of eyes.

Romeo apparently has never played hide-and-go-seek.

[Knocking.]

FRIAR LAURENCE

Hark, how they knock! Who's there? Romeo, arise;
Thou wilt be taken. Stay awhile! Stand up;

[Knocking.]

Run to my study. By and by! God's will,
What simpleness is this! I come, I come!

[Knocking.]

Who knocks so hard? whence come you? what's your will?

NURSE

[Within.] Let me come in, and you shall know
my errand;
I come from Lady Juliet.

FRIAR LAURENCE

Welcome, then.

Enter NURSE

NURSE

O holy Friar, O, tell me, holy Friar,
Where is my lady's lord, where's Romeo?

FRIAR LAURENCE

There on the ground, with his own tears made drunk.

Father Larry! That's not how the game is played!

NURSE

O, he is even in my mistress' case,
Just in her case! O woeful sympathy!
Piteous predicament! Even so lies she,
Blubbering and weeping, weeping and blubbering.
Stand up, stand up; stand, an you be a man:
For Juliet's sake, for her sake, rise and stand;
Why should you fall into so deep an O?

"O": an expression of grief.

ROMEO

Nurse!

NURSE

Ah sir! ah sir! Well, death's the end of all.

There's a fine howdy-do!

ROMEO

Spakest thou of Juliet? how is it with her?
Doth she not think me an old murderer,
Now I have stain'd the childhood of our joy

Romeo is worried that Juliet has stopped loving him because of the killing of Tybalt.

With blood removed but little from her own?
Where is she? and how doth she? and what says
My conceal'd lady to our cancell'd love?

"conceal'd lady": secretly married.

NURSE

O, she says nothing, sir, but weeps and weeps;
And now falls on her bed; and then starts up,
And Tybalt calls; and then on Romeo cries,
And then down falls again.

ROMEO

As if that name,
Shot from the deadly level of a gun,
Did murder her; as that name's cursed hand
Murder'd her kinsman. O, tell me, Friar, tell me,
In what vile part of this anatomy
Doth my name lodge? tell me, that I may sack
The hateful mansion.

Romeo wants to kill himself. (He can't yet, it's only Act III!)

[Drawing his sword.]

FRIAR LAURENCE

Hold thy desperate hand:
Art thou a man? thy form cries out thou art:
Thy tears are womanish; thy wild acts denote
The unreasonable fury of a beast:
Unseemly woman in a seeming man!
And ill-beseeming beast in seeming both!
Thou hast amazed me: by my holy order,
I thought thy disposition better temper'd.
Hast thou slain Tybalt? wilt thou slay thyself?
And slay thy lady that in thy life lives,
By doing damned hate upon thyself?
Why rail'st thou on thy birth, the heaven, and earth?
Since birth, and heaven, and earth, all three do meet
In thee at once; which thou at once wouldst lose.
Fie, fie, thou shamest thy shape, thy love, thy wit;
Which, like a usurer, abound'st in all,
And usest none in that true use indeed
Which should bedeck thy shape, thy love, thy wit:
Thy noble shape is but a form of wax,
Digressing from the valour of a man;
Thy dear love sworn but hollow perjury,
Killing that love which thou hast vow'd to cherish;
Thy wit, that ornament to shape and love,
Misshapen in the conduct of them both,
Like powder in a skilless soldier's flask,
Is set afire by thine own ignorance,
And thou dismember'd with thine own defence.
What, rouse thee, man! thy Juliet is alive,
For whose dear sake thou wast but lately dead;
There art thou happy: Tybalt would kill thee,
But thou slew'st Tybalt; there art thou happy:
The law that threaten'd death becomes thy friend

Father Larry takes one long, deep breath, and he's off!

"ill-beseeming": it is inappropriate for a man to behave this way.

"defence": weapon.

And turns it to exile; there art thou happy:
A pack of blessings lights upon thy back;
Happiness courts thee in her best array;
But, like a misbehaved and sullen wench,
Thou pout'st upon thy fortune and thy love:
Take heed, take heed, for such die miserable.
Go, get thee to thy love, as was decreed,
Ascend her chamber, hence and comfort her:
But look thou stay not till the watch be set,
For then thou canst not pass to Mantua;
Where thou shalt live, till we can find a time
To blaze your marriage, reconcile your friends,
Beg pardon of the Prince, and call thee back
With twenty hundred thousand times more joy
Than thou went'st forth in lamentation.
Go before, nurse: commend me to thy lady;
And bid her hasten all the house to bed,
Which heavy sorrow makes them apt unto:
Romeo is coming.

NURSE

O Lord, I could have stay'd here all the night
To hear good counsel: O, what learning is!
My lord, I'll tell my lady you will come.

ROMEO

Do so, and bid my sweet prepare to chide.

NURSE

Here, sir, a ring she bid me give you, sir:
Hie you, make haste, for it grows very late.

Exit

ROMEO

How well my comfort is revived by this!

FRIAR LAURENCE

Go hence; good night; and here stands all your state:
Either be gone before the watch be set,
Or by the break of day disguised from hence:
Sojourn in Mantua; I'll find out your man,
And he shall signify from time to time
Every good hap to you that chances here:
Give me thy hand; 'tis late: farewell; good night.

ROMEO

But that a joy past joy calls out on me,
It were a grief, so brief to part with thee: Farewell.

Exeunt

Yeah, comfort - that's what you want on your wedding night.

Father Larry instructs the Nurse to make sure the Capulets go to bed so Romeo can. . .uh, comfort, yeah, comfort Juliet.

Well, if Father Larry's last speech is any indication, it might take all night.

Tell her, "Romeo is on his way!"

At least she didn't take it to a pawn shop.

"Well, I feel better!"

Here's what you do: leave Juliet before the sun comes up and chill in Mantua; I'll keep you up on the haps.

Act III, Scene IV

Scene Synopsis

Paris, the horn-dawg, insists that he be allowed to marry Juliet. Capulet, in his infinite wisdom, agrees that the marriage should take place in three days. Now, the plot thickens! And we see that in this world, adults can also be impulsive.

Scene IV

A room in Capulet's house.

Enter CAPULET, LADY CAPULET, and PARIS

CAPULET

> Things have fall'n out, sir, so unluckily,
> That we have had no time to move our daughter:
> Look you, she loved her kinsman Tybalt dearly,
> And so did I:--Well, we were born to die.
> 'Tis very late, she'll not come down tonight:
> I promise you, but for your company,
> I would have been abed an hour ago.

You can say this for Paris, he's persistent.

Translation: "We've been through enough today. Cool your jets, Paris."

PARIS

> These times of woe afford no time to woo.
> Madam, good night: commend me to your daughter.

LADY CAPULET

> I will, and know her mind early tomorrow;
> Tonight she's mew'd up to her heaviness.

CAPULET

> Sir Paris, I will make a desperate tender
> Of my child's love: I think she will be ruled
> In all respects by me; nay, more, I doubt it not.
> Wife, go you to her ere you go to bed;
> Acquaint her here of my son Paris' love;
> And bid her, mark you me, on Wednesday next--
> But, soft! what day is this?

Lord Capulet, even in mourning, never misses the opportunity to broker a deal.

Not so fast, L.C.!

Paris is supposed to trust a guy who doesn't even know what day it is?

PARIS

> Monday, my lord

CAPULET

> Monday! ha, ha! Well, Wednesday is too soon,
> O' Thursday let it be: a Thursday, tell her,
> She shall be married to this noble earl.
> Will you be ready? do you like this haste?
> We'll keep no great ado,--a friend or two;
> For, hark you, Tybalt being slain so late,
> It may be thought we held him carelessly,
> Being our kinsman, if we revel much:
> Therefore we'll have some half a dozen friends,
> And there an end. But what say you to Thursday?

L.C. apparently likes Mondays. "O' Thursday" or "On Thursday."

L.C. attempts to be sensitive to Tybalt's death.

PARIS

> My lord, I would that Thursday were tomorrow.

CAPULET

> Well get you gone: a Thursday be it, then.
> Go you to Juliet ere you go to bed,

L.C., again, talks to three people at once. Does this guy have a problem or what?

Prepare her, wife, against this wedding day.
Farewell, my lord. Light to my chamber, ho!
Afore me! it is so very very late,
That we may call it early by and by.
Good night.

Exeunt

Shakespeare uses this line to tell the audience what time it is: about 4 or 5 a.m.

⤳ Act III, Scene V ⤳

Scene Synopsis

Juliet kisses Romeo good-bye as the sun comes up. Her parents and the Nurse enter to tell her of the wedding plans. She freaks out, they get mad, threats are made, and Juliet decides Father Larry is the only one who can help her.

Scene V
Juliet's chamber.

Enter ROMEO and JULIET, above, at the window

Time plays a major role in increasing the tension of this scene. Romeo, according to Father Larry, needs to be gone by sun up.

JULIET

Wilt thou be gone? it is not yet near day:
It was the nightingale, and not the lark,
That pierced the fearful hollow of thine ear;
Nightly she sings on yon pomegranate tree:
Believe me, love, it was the nightingale.

Juliet tries to convince Romeo that he can stay with her longer. The nightingale often sings at night; the lark, during the first light of day.

ROMEO

It was the lark, the herald of the morn,
No nightingale: look, love, what envious streaks
Do lace the severing clouds in yonder east:
Night's candles are burnt out, and jocund day
Stands tiptoe on the misty mountain tops.
I must be gone and live, or stay and die.

"Listen, it's been fun, but I gotta go."

Personification: daylight taking on human qualities: "stands tiptoe."

JULIET

Yon light is not daylight, I know it, I:
It is some meteor that the sun exhales,
To be to thee this night a torchbearer,
And light thee on thy way to Mantua:
Therefore stay yet; thou need'st not to be gone.

What about "I gotta go" does she not understand?

ROMEO

Let me be ta'en, let me be put to death;
I am content, so thou wilt have it so.
I'll say yon grey is not the morning's eye,
'Tis but the pale reflex of Cynthia's brow;
Nor that is not the lark, whose notes do beat
The vaulty heaven so high above our heads:
I have more care to stay than will to go:
Come, death, and welcome! Juliet wills it so.
How is't, my soul? let's talk; it is not day.

Ah, the power of love! Romeo chooses death over leaving his honey.

"Cynthia": a reference to Diana, goddess of the moon.

Is this guy committed or what?

JULIET

It is, it is: hie hence, be gone, away!
It is the lark that sings so out of tune,
Straining harsh discords and unpleasing sharps.

When did she figure this out? Indecision, thy name is Juliet.

Some say the lark makes sweet division;
This doth not so, for she divideth us:
Some say the lark and loathed toad change eyes,
O, now I would they had changed voices too!
Since arm from arm that voice doth us affray,
Hunting thee hence with hunt's-up to the day,
O, now be gone; more light and light it grows.

ROMEO

More light and light; more dark and dark our woes!

Enter NURSE, to the chamber

NURSE

Madam!

JULIET

Nurse?

NURSE

Your lady mother is coming to your chamber:
The day is broke; be wary, look about.

Exit

JULIET

Then, window, let day in, and let life out.

ROMEO

Farewell, farewell! one kiss, and I'll descend.

[He goes down.]

JULIET

Art thou gone so? love, lord, ay, husband, friend!
I must hear from thee every day in the hour,
For in a minute there are many days:
O, by this count I shall be much in years
Ere I again behold my Romeo!

ROMEO

Farewell!
I will omit no opportunity
That may convey my greetings, love, to thee.

JULIET

O think'st thou we shall ever meet again?

ROMEO

I doubt it not; and all these woes shall serve
For sweet discourses in our time to come.

JULIET

O God, I have an ill-divining soul!
Methinks I see thee, now thou art so low,
As one dead in the bottom of a tomb:
Either my eyesight fails, or thou look'st pale.

ROMEO

And trust me, love, in my eye so do you:
Dry sorrow drinks our blood. Adieu, adieu!

Exit

"sweet division": sweet melody.

"hunt's-up": song to waken hunters.
Notice how Romeo completes this couplet line with "woes."

(Let's see how long it takes for her to get to the point.)

Heads up, Juliet!

(Hey, nice job, Nurse!)

No, she didn't jump! She's talking about daylight and Romeo's departure.

Yeah, right. These two have never been good at short good-byes. This is what's called "an Irish good-bye": long and tearful.

Translation: "I'll miss you."

Translation: "I'll hollah."

It's a nice thought, but they don't meet again.

"We're going to look back on this someday and laugh." Nice thought, but they do neither.

Now, this is what you want to hear if you're Romeo: "You look like a dead guy."

Yes, it's foreshadowing, again.

Well, it takes one to know one. Sorrow was thought to 'dry up' the blood. This is typical of Renaissance thinking, based on the "four humors."

JULIET

    O fortune, fortune! all men call thee fickle:
    If thou art fickle, what dost thou with him.
    That is renown'd for faith? Be fickle, fortune;
    For then, I hope, thou wilt not keep him long,
    But send him back.

Juliet mentions fortune or fate. Shakespeare's images of opposition indicate how R & J have tempted fate.

LADY CAPULET

    [*Within.*] Ho, daughter! are you up?

"Ho": a call for attention.

JULIET

    Who is't that calls? is it my lady mother?
    Is she not down so late, or up so early?
    What unaccustom'd cause procures her hither?

"What has happened that she should be awake?"

Enter LADY CAPULET

LADY CAPULET

    Why, how now, Juliet!

"Why are you awake?"

JULIET

    Madam, I am not well.

Juliet must think it's a school day.

LADY CAPULET

    Evermore weeping for your cousin's death?
    What, wilt thou wash him from his grave with tears?
    An if thou couldst, thou couldst not make him live;
    Therefore, have done: some grief shows much of love;
    But much of grief shows still some want of wit.

Translation: "Enough, already! Build a bridge and get over it."

JULIET

    Yet let me weep for such a feeling loss.

Lady Capulet thinks Juliet is crying over Tybalt; it's Romeo for whom she weeps.

LADY CAPULET

    So shall you feel the loss, but not the friend
    Which you weep for.

"Crying won't bring him back."

JULIET

    Feeling so the loss,
    I cannot choose but ever weep the friend.

"I can't help it."

LADY CAPULET

    Well, girl, thou weep'st not so much for his death,
    As that the villain lives which slaughter'd him.

JULIET

    What villain madam?

LADY CAPULET

    That same villain, Romeo.

JULIET

    [*Aside.*] Villain and he be many miles asunder.--
    God Pardon him! I do, with all my heart;
    And yet no man like he doth grieve my heart.

In an "Aside," the character speaks, but only the audience can hear the words.

LADY CAPULET

    That is, because the traitor murderer lives.

JULIET

    Ay, madam, from the reach of these my hands:
    Would none but I might venge my cousin's death!

Get the double meaning? Juliet would like to "reach" Romeo.

LADY CAPULET

We will have vengeance for it, fear thou not:
Then weep no more. I'll send to one in Mantua,
Where that same banish'd runagate doth live,
Shall give him such an unaccustom'd dram,
That he shall soon keep Tybalt company:
And then, I hope, thou wilt be satisfied.

Lady Capulet plans to kill Romeo with a poison potion or "dram."

JULIET

Indeed, I never shall be satisfied
With Romeo, till I behold him—dead—
Is my poor heart for a kinsman vex'd.
Madam, if you could find out but a man
To bear a poison, I would temper it;
That Romeo should, upon receipt thereof,
Soon sleep in quiet. O, how my heart abhors
To hear him named, and cannot come to him.
To wreak the love I bore my cousin
Upon his body that hath slaughter'd him!

Juliet chooses her words carefully—as conveyed by the dash—to please her mother.

Double meaning: Juliet says hate, but means love.

LADY CAPULET

Find thou the means, and I'll find such a man.
But now I'll tell thee joyful tidings, girl.

JULIET

And joy comes well in such a needy time:
What are they, I beseech your ladyship?

LADY CAPULET

Well, well, thou hast a careful father, child;
One who, to put thee from thy heaviness,
Hath sorted out a sudden day of joy,
That thou expect'st not nor I look'd not for.

Lady Capulet obviously learned to speak at the Father Larry School of Brevity.

JULIET

Madam, in happy time, what day is that?

LADY CAPULET

Marry, my child, early next Thursday morn,
The gallant, young and noble gentleman,
The County Paris, at Saint Peter's Church,
Shall happily make thee there a joyful bride.

JULIET

Now, by Saint Peter's Church and Peter too,
He shall not make me there a joyful bride.
I wonder at this haste; that I must wed
Ere he, that should be husband, comes to woo.
I pray you, tell my lord and father, madam,
I will not marry yet; and, when I do, I swear,
It shall be Romeo, whom you know I hate,
Rather than Paris. These are news indeed!

Just a guess: probably not the best timing, Lady C.

Nice save, Juliet!

LADY CAPULET

Here comes your father; tell him so yourself,
And see how he will take it at your hands.

Enter CAPULET and NURSE

CAPULET

    When the sun sets, the earth doth drizzle dew;
    But for the sunset of my brother's son
    It rains downright.
    How now! a conduit, girl? what, still in tears?
    Evermore showering? In one little body
    Thou counterfeit'st a bark, a sea, a wind;
    For still thy eyes, which I may call the sea,
    Do ebb and flow with tears; the bark thy body is,
    Sailing in this salt flood; the winds, thy sighs;
    Who, raging with thy tears, and they with them,
    Without a sudden calm, will overset
    Thy tempest-tossed body. How now, wife!
    Have you deliver'd to her our decree?

> Just what we need: a long speech of wisdom from Lord Capulet.

> Wow, Master of the Obvious: he noticed that she's crying.

LADY CAPULET

    Ay, sir; but she will none, she gives you thanks.
    I would the fool were married to her grave!

> Be careful what you wish for!

CAPULET

    Soft! take me with you, take me with you, wife.
    How! will she none? doth she not give us thanks?
    Is she not proud? doth she not count her blest,
    Unworthy as she is, that we have wrought
    So worthy a gentleman to be her bride?

> Somebody stop him before he pops a vein.

> "wrought": secured.

JULIET

    Not proud, you have; but thankful, that you have:
    Proud can I never be of what I hate;
    But thankful even for hate, that is meant love.

> Juliet is just about to go right over the old man's head.

CAPULET

    How now, how now, chopped logic! What is this?
    'Proud,' and 'I thank you,' and 'I thank you not;'
    And yet 'not proud?' Mistress minion, you,
    Thank me no thankings, nor, proud me no prouds,
    But fettle your fine joints 'gainst Thursday next,
    To go with Paris to Saint Peter's Church,
    Or I will drag thee on a hurdle thither.
    Out, you green-sickness carrion! out, you baggage!
    You tallow-face!

> "chopped logic": sophistry or double-talk.

> Translation: He's mad.

> "green-sickness": an anemia that affected young girls. Often associated with virginity. Guess what the doctor's advice was.

LADY CAPULET

    Fie, fie! what, are you mad?

> It's clear that this "Master of the Obvious" thing is a family trait.

JULIET

    Good father, I beseech you on my knees,
    Hear me with patience but to speak a word.

CAPULET

    Hang thee, young baggage! disobedient wretch!
    I tell thee what: get thee to church a Thursday,
    Or never after look me in the face:
    Speak not, reply not, do not answer me;
    My fingers itch. Wife, we scarce thought us blest

> Now, she asked nicely, didn't she?

> "fingers itch": to hit her.

That God had lent us but this only child;
But now I see this one is one too much,
And that we have a curse in having her:
Out on her, hilding!

NURSE

God in heaven bless her!
You are to blame, my lord, to rate her so.

That's it, Nurse! Insult a
screaming man!

CAPULET

And why, my Lady Wisdom? hold your tongue,
Good prudence; smatter with your gossips, go.

"Lady Wisdom": can you say
sarcasm?

"smatter": go chat and dish
with your girls.

NURSE

I speak no treason.

CAPULET

O, God ye god-den.

"God ye god-den": God grant
you a good evening. Good-bye.

NURSE

May not one speak?

You can, but he's not listening to
you.

CAPULET

Peace, you mumbling fool!
Utter your gravity o'er a gossip's bowl;
For here we need it not.

Talk to other people who gossip
– not me!

LADY CAPULET

You are too hot.

See? Mistress of the Obvious.

CAPULET

God's bread! it makes me mad:
Day, night, hour, tide, time, work, play,

You don't say? You? Mad?
Nah!!!!!!!!!

Alone, in company, still my care hath been
To have her match'd: and having now provided
A gentleman of noble parentage,
Of fair demesnes, youthful, and nobly train'd,
Stuff'd, as they say, with honourable parts,
Proportion'd as one's thought would wish a man;
And then to have a wretched puling fool,
A whining mammet, in her fortune's tender,
To answer 'I'll not wed; I cannot love,
I am too young; I pray you, pardon me.'
But, an you will not wed, I'll pardon you:
Graze where you will you shall not house with me:
Look to't, think on't, I do not use to jest.
Thursday is near; lay hand on heart, advise:
An you be mine, I'll give you to my friend;
An you be not, hang, beg, starve, die in the streets,
For, by my soul, I'll ne'er acknowledge thee,
Nor what is mine shall never do thee good:
Trust to't, bethink you; I'll not be forsworn.

"demesnes": estates, property.

"puling fool": a whiner.

"mammet": a doll or plaything.

If Juliet doesn't agree to marry
Paris, her father is going to
disown her. (And that's a
threat?) Notice how hot-headed
these men are.

Exit

JULIET

Is there no pity sitting in the clouds,
That sees into the bottom of my grief?

Elizabethan staging of this
scene indicates that Juliet's

O, sweet my mother, cast me not away!
Delay this marriage for a month, a week;
Or, if you do not, make the bridal bed
In that dim monument where Tybalt lies.

LADY CAPULET

Talk not to me, for I'll not speak a word:
Do as thou wilt, for I have done with thee.

Exit

JULIET

O God!—O Nurse, how shall this be prevented?
My husband is on earth, my faith in heaven;
How shall that faith return again to earth,
Unless that husband send it me from heaven
By leaving earth? comfort me, counsel me.
Alack, alack, that heaven should practise stratagems
Upon so soft a subject as myself!
What say'st thou? hast thou not a word of joy?
Some comfort, Nurse.

NURSE

Faith, here it is.
Romeo is banish'd; and all the world to nothing,
That he dares ne'er come back to challenge you;
Or, if he do, it needs must be by stealth.
Then, since the case so stands as now it doth,
I think it best you married with the County.
O, he's a lovely gentleman!
Romeo's a dishclout to him: an eagle, madam,
Hath not so green, so quick, so fair an eye
As Paris hath. Beshrew my very heart,
I think you are happy in this second match,
For it excels your first: or if it did not,
Your first is dead; or 'twere as good he were,
As living here and you no use of him.

JULIET

Speakest thou from thy heart?

NURSE

And from my soul too;
else beshrew them both.

JULIET

Amen!

NURSE

What?

JULIET

Well, thou hast comforted me marvellous much.
Go in: and tell my lady I am gone,
Having displeased my father, to Laurence' cell,
To make confession and to be absolved.

NURSE

Marry, I will; and this is wisely done.

---

bedchamber may very well have doubled as her tomb, reinforcing the textual themes of love/hate and death/marriage.

Hmmm. . .dis'd by your mom – that can't be good.

An interesting thought: Romeo and Juliet are together in eternity.

Betrayal? In her moment of greatest need, the Nurse wants her to marry Paris, when she knows that Juliet loves Romeo.

"dishclout": a dishcloth.

Typical Teen: Look at Juliet's last speech. Clearly she was thinking of her plan and not listening to an adult - even if it is the Nurse speaking.

JULIET

Ancient damnation! O most wicked fiend!
Is it more sin to wish me thus forsworn,
Or to dispraise my lord with that same tongue
Which she hath praised him with above compare
So many thousand times? Go, counsellor;
Thou and my bosom henceforth shall be twain.
I'll to the Friar, to know his remedy:
If all else fail, myself have power to die.

Exit

Juliet dismisses the Nurse's advice and decides to go to Father Larry instead.

Act III Notes

Act III Notes

Act III Notes

Act III Notes

Romeo and Juliet
～ Act IV, Scene I ～
Scene Synopsis

Impatient Paris tries to hurry Father Larry to set a time for Juliet and himself to be married. Father Larry now has a problem.

Scene I
Friar Laurence's cell.

Enter FRIAR LAURENCE and PARIS

FRIAR LAURENCE
> On Thursday, sir? the time is very short.

Ah. . .the act of stalling for time.

PARIS
> My father Capulet will have it so;
> And I am nothing slow to slack his haste.

"nothing slow to slack his haste": I don't want to slow him down.

FRIAR LAURENCE
> You say you do not know the lady's mind:
> Uneven is the course, I like it not.

"Uneven is the course": This is not going to be easy. (If Paris only knew!)

PARIS
> Immoderately she weeps for Tybalt's death,
> And therefore have I little talk'd of love;
> For Venus smiles not in a house of tears.
> Now, sir, her father counts it dangerous
> That she do give her sorrow so much sway,
> And in his wisdom hastes our marriage,
> To stop the inundation of her tears;
> Which, too much minded by herself alone,
> May be put from her by society:
> Now do you know the reason of this haste.

It's hard to read Paris' character. Is he truly concerned about Juliet? Is he just trying to follow Lord Capulet's wishes, or is it the business deal of Juliet's family money and taking advantage of the family during a time of emotional weakness?

FRIAR LAURENCE
> [*Aside.*] I would I knew not why it should be slow'd.
> Look, sir, here comes the lady toward my cell.

You should have thought of that, Father!

Enter JULIET

PARIS
> Happily met, my lady and my wife!

Well, young Paris is assuming a great deal now, isn't he!

JULIET
> That may be, sir, when I may be a wife.

Didn't he just say she was sad?

Paris, the operative word here is "may."

PARIS
> That may be must be, love, on Thursday next.

Pushy, pushy!

JULIET
> What must be shall be.

Now that's an enthusiastic response for a wife-to-be.

FRIAR LAURENCE
> That's a certain text.

That Father Larry never misses the opportunity for a rhyme.

PARIS
> Come you to make confession to this father?

Slow your roll, Paris! Dang, man!

JULIET
> To answer that, I should confess to you.

"Get a clue, dude - I'm not talking to you!"

PARIS

> Do not deny to him that you love me.

JULIET

> I will confess to you that I love him.

PARIS

> So will ye, I am sure, that you love me.

JULIET

> If I do so, it will be of more price,
> Being spoke behind your back, than to your face.

PARIS

> Poor soul, thy face is much abused with tears.

JULIET

> The tears have got small victory by that;
> For it was bad enough before their spite.

PARIS

> Thou wrong'st it, more than tears, with that report.

JULIET

> That is no slander, sir, which is a truth;
> And what I spake, I spake it to my face.

PARIS

> Thy face is mine, and thou hast slander'd it.

JULIET

> It may be so, for it is not mine own.
> Are you at leisure, holy father, now;
> Or shall I come to you at evening mass?

FRIAR LAURENCE

> My leisure serves me, pensive daughter, now.
> My lord, we must entreat the time alone.

PARIS

> God shield I should disturb devotion!
> Juliet, on Thursday early will I rouse ye:
> Till then, adieu; and keep this holy kiss.

Exit

JULIET

> O shut the door! and when thou hast done so,
> Come weep with me; past hope, past cure, past help!

FRIAR LAURENCE

> Ah, Juliet, I already know thy grief;
> It strains me past the compass of my wits:
> I hear thou must, and nothing may prorogue it,
> On Thursday next be married to this County.

JULIET

> Tell me not, Friar, that thou hear'st of this,
> Unless thou tell me how I may prevent it:
> If, in thy wisdom, thou canst give no help,
> Do thou but call my resolution wise,
> And with this knife I'll help it presently.

Is Paris stupid, single-minded, or. . .?

"Do I have to draw you a picture?"

"him": the Friar and/or Romeo.

Next to the definition of a "bad date" is a picture of Paris.

Situational irony: the audience knows what Juliet means; Paris (of course) does not.

And her eyes too much abused to look at you!

Juliet tries to dissuade Paris from thinking her face is beautiful.

Paris doesn't get it (surprise!).

He just doesn't quit, does he?

Juliet tries to dismiss Paris (finally) by making an appointment to speak with Father Larry.

"Paris, don't let the door hit you in the butt on your way out!"

Yeah, good luck with all that, Paris!

And we thought Romeo was the raging hormone!

Not terribly optimistic, is she?

"prorogue": postpone.

While the '68 film had Juliet threaten suicide with a knife, the '96 film showed Juliet with a gun, cocked and pointed at her head.

God join'd my heart and Romeo's, thou our hands;
And ere this hand, by thee to Romeo's seal'd,
Shall be the label to another deed,
Or my true heart with treacherous revolt
Turn to another, this shall slay them both:
Therefore, out of thy long-experienced time,
Give me some present counsel, or, behold,
'Twixt my extremes and me this bloody knife
Shall play the umpire, arbitrating that
Which the commission of thy years and art
Could to no issue of true honour bring.
Be not so long to speak; I long to die,
If what thou speak'st speak not of remedy.

FRIAR LAURENCE
Hold, daughter: I do spy a kind of hope,
Which craves as desperate an execution.
As that is desperate which we would prevent.
If, rather than to marry County Paris,
Thou hast the strength of will to slay thyself,
Then is it likely thou wilt undertake
A thing like death to chide away this shame,
That cop'st with death himself to scape from it:
And, if thou darest, I'll give thee remedy.

JULIET
O, bid me leap, rather than marry Paris,
From off the battlements of any tower;
Or walk in thievish ways; or bid me lurk
Where serpents are; chain me with roaring bears;
Or hide me nightly in a charnel-house,
O'ercover'd quite with dead men's rattling bones,
With reeky shanks and yellow chapless skulls;
Or bid me go into a new-made grave
And hide me with a dead man in his shroud;
Things that, to hear them told, have made me tremble;
And I will do it without fear or doubt,
To live an unstain'd wife to my sweet love.

FRIAR LAURENCE
Hold, then; go home, be merry, give consent
To marry Paris: Wednesday is tomorrow:
Tomorrow night look that thou lie alone;
Let not thy Nurse lie with thee in thy chamber:
Take thou this vial, being then in bed,
And this distilling liquor drink thou off;
When presently through all thy veins shall run
A cold and drowsy humour, for no pulse
Shall keep his native progress, but surcease:
No warmth, no breath, shall testify thou livest;
The roses in thy lips and cheeks shall fade
To wanny ashes, thy eyes' windows fall,
Like death, when he shuts up the day of life;
Each part, deprived of supple government,

Juliet's desperate mental state forces Father Larry to think quickly. What other options does Juliet have?

Father Larry reminds us of his first speech about herbs; like men, they can be both good and evil.

Well, she is considering options: jumping off a wall instead of stabbing herself.

"a new-made grave": this is the line that gives Father Larry the idea of an herb that will make Juliet *appear* dead so her marriage to Paris will be cancelled and she can escape later with Romeo.

Hey, what an excuse to get out of going to school! Uhhh. . .no, consider what happens at the end of the play. Even missing a test is not worth that!

Shall, stiff and stark and cold, appear like death:
And in this borrow'd likeness of shrunk death
Thou shalt continue two and forty hours,
And then awake as from a pleasant sleep.
Now, when the bridegroom in the morning comes
To rouse thee from thy bed, there art thou dead:
Then, as the manner of our country is,
In thy best robes uncover'd on the bier
Thou shalt be borne to that same ancient vault
Where all the kindred of the Capulets lie.
In the meantime, against thou shalt awake,
Shall Romeo by my letters know our drift,
And hither shall he come: and he and I
Will watch thy waking, and that very night
Shall Romeo bear thee hence to Mantua.
And this shall free thee from this present shame;
If no inconstant toy, nor womanish fear,
Abate thy valour in the acting it.

JULIET

Give me, give me! O, tell not me of fear!

FRIAR LAURENCE

Hold; get you gone, be strong and prosperous
In this resolve: I'll send a friar with speed
To Mantua, with my letters to thy lord.

JULIET

Love give me strength! and strength shall help afford.
Farewell, dear father!

Exeunt

"two and forty hours":
Shakespeare doesn't allow two
days to pass before Juliet
awakens. Mistake or poetic/
dramatic license?

Here's the plan: Juliet's family will
think she's dead and place her in
the burial tomb beside Tybalt,
who is probably beginning to
smell by now! And Father Larry
will send a letter to Romeo
(written in Seuss-like verse, no
doubt) telling him Juliet is *not*
really dead. This letter proves to
be the fatal flaw (literally) of the
plan.

Wow! Not much need of
convincing her.

"a friar with speed": in the '68
film it was a man on a donkey.
The donkey, of course, is one of
nature's fastest animals, just
above the turtle.

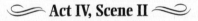

∽ Act IV, Scene II ∽
Scene Synopsis

The Capulets prepare for the wedding and Juliet, in an Academy Award performance, agrees to the marriage. Capulet is psyched!

Scene II
Hall in Capulet's house.

Enter CAPULET, LADY CAPULET, NURSE, and two or three SERVINGMEN

CAPULET

So many guests invite as here are writ.

Exit a SERVINGMAN

Sirrah, go hire me twenty cunning cooks.

SERVINGMAN

You shall have none ill, sir; for I'll try if they
can lick their fingers.

CAPULET

How canst thou try them so?

Here we go again. A meeting of
the minds: Lord Capulet and the
servants.

Notice what Shakespeare does
here: comic relief in a serious
situation.

The servant is talking over
Capulet's head (surprise!).

SERVINGMAN

Marry, sir, 'tis an ill cook that cannot lick his
own fingers: therefore he that cannot lick his
fingers goes not with me.

CAPULET

Go, be gone.

Exit SERVINGMAN

We shall be much unfurnished for this time.
What, is my daughter gone to Friar Laurence?

NURSE

Ay, forsooth.

CAPULET

Well, he may chance to do some good on her:
A peevish self-will'd harlotry it is.

NURSE

See where she comes from shrift with merry look.

Enter JULIET

CAPULET

How now, my headstrong! where have you been gadding?

JULIET

Where I have learnt me to repent the sin
Of disobedient opposition
To you and your behests, and am enjoin'd
By holy Laurence to fall prostrate here,
To beg your pardon: pardon, I beseech you!
Henceforward I am ever ruled by you.

CAPULET

Send for the County; go tell him of this:
I'll have this knot knit up tomorrow morning.

JULIET

I met the youthful lord at Laurence' cell;
And gave him what becomed love I might,
Not stepping o'er the bounds of modesty.

CAPULET

Why, I am glad on't; this is well: stand up:
This is as't should be. Let me see the County;
Ay, marry, go, I say, and fetch him hither.
Now, afore God! this reverend Holy Friar,
All our whole city is much bound to him.

JULIET

Nurse, will you go with me into my closet,
To help me sort such needful ornaments
As you think fit to furnish me tomorrow?

LADY CAPULET

No, not till Thursday; there is time enough.

CAPULET

Go, Nurse, go with her: we'll to church tomorrow.

Exeunt JULIET and NURSE

In Elizabethan times, a cook who
would not eat his/her own
cooking was not trusted. And the
early Greeks and Romans had
official "tasters" as security
against murder by poisoning.

"much unfurnished for this time":
a recurring theme with Capulet -
wasn't he also "unfurnished" for
the party in Act I?

"harlotry": Capulet doesn't mean
that Juliet is a harlot, just a
moody teen.

Translation: "Dad, I'm sorry. You
were right and I am wrong. (Try
this, admitting your parents were
right - even if they're not. Hey, it
works for Juliet!)

The ever-patient Capulet.

Again, Juliet plays the middle
ground of ambiguity: "I didn't
say I loved him, but I didn't say
I didn't, either."

Capulet has no idea how "bound"
or involved Father Larry is in this
ordeal.

Translation: "I'm going to pretend
to die. Will you help me get
ready?"

LADY CAPULET

> We shall be short in our provision:
> 'Tis now near night.

CAPULET

> Tush, I will stir about,
> And all things shall be well, I warrant thee, wife:
> Go thou to Juliet, help to deck up her;
> I'll not to bed tonight; let me alone;
> I'll play the housewife for this once. What, ho!
> They are all forth. Well, I will walk myself
> To County Paris, to prepare him up
> Against tomorrow: my heart is wondrous light,
> Since this same wayward girl is so reclaim'd.

Be careful, L.C. is in charge!

What a picture! Lord Capulet in a nice flower-print apron and six-inch heels.

He bought it—hook, line, and sinker.

Exeunt

∽ Act IV, Scene III ∽

Scene Synopsis

Juliet successfully dismisses her Nurse and mother. After considering all of the bad things that could happen, she drinks the potion and falls on her bed in a trance. I hope her room is clean!

Scene III
Juliet's chamber.

Enter JULIET and NURSE

JULIET

> Ay, those attires are best: but, gentle Nurse,
> I pray thee, leave me to myself tonight,
> For I have need of many orisons
> To move the heavens to smile upon my state,
> Which, well thou know'st, is cross, and full of sin.

"orisons": prayers.

Translation: "I need to be alone because I've got a few things on my mind, like I'm already married and I'm going to pretend to die."

Enter LADY CAPULET

LADY CAPULET

> What, are you busy, ho? need you my help?

Now she asks.

JULIET

> No, madam; we have cull'd such necessaries
> As are behoveful for our state tomorrow:
> So please you, let me now be left alone,
> And let the Nurse this night sit up with you;
> For, I am sure, you have your hands full all,
> In this so sudden business.

"What part of 'leave me alone' don't you understand?"

LADY CAPULET

> Good night:
> Get thee to bed, and rest; for thou hast need.

Oh, she'll rest all right.

Exeunt LADY CAPULET and NURSE

JULIET

> Farewell! God knows when we shall meet again.
> I have a faint cold fear thrills through my veins,
> That almost freezes up the heat of life:
> I'll call them back again to comfort me:

Juliet plays the pessimistic "what if" game with herself.

Nurse! What should she do here?
My dismal scene I needs must act alone.
Come, vial.
What if this mixture do not work at all?
Shall I be married then tomorrow morning?
No, no: this shall forbid it: lie thou there.

[Laying down her dagger.]

That's a good girl, put the knife down.

What if it be a poison, which the Friar
Subtly hath minister'd to have me dead,
Lest in this marriage he should be dishonour'd,
Because he married me before to Romeo?
I fear it is: and yet, methinks, it should not,
For he hath still been tried a holy man.
How if, when I am laid into the tomb,
I wake before the time that Romeo
Come to redeem me? there's a fearful point!

Not as scary as the point of a knife.

Shall I not, then, be stifled in the vault,
To whose foul mouth no healthsome air breathes in,
And there die strangled ere my Romeo comes?
Or, if I live, is it not very like,
The horrible conceit of death and night,
Together with the terror of the place,--
As in a vault, an ancient receptacle,
Where, for these many hundred years, the bones
Of all my buried ancestors are packed:
Where bloody Tybalt, yet but green in earth,
Lies festering in his shroud; where, as they say,
At some hours in the night spirits resort;--
Alack, alack, is it not like that I,
So early waking, what with loathsome smells,
And shrieks like mandrakes torn out of the earth,
That living mortals, hearing them, run mad:--
O, if I wake, shall I not be distraught,
Environed with all these hideous fears?
And madly play with my forefathers' joints?
And pluck the mangled Tybalt from his shroud?
And, in this rage, with some great kinsman's bone,
As with a club, dash out my desperate brains?
O, look! methinks I see my cousin's ghost
Seeking out Romeo, that did spit his body
Upon a rapier's point: stay, Tybalt, stay!
Romeo, I come! this do I drink to thee.

The mandrake was a popular ingredient in sleeping potions. Elizabethans believed the forked root of the mandrake resembled a human figure that would scream when pulled up and drive the bearer mad.

Many Shakespearean critics believe that the suspense of this scene and the following scenes is increased by the fact that only curtains separate Juliet from the audience.

[She falls upon her bed, within the curtains.]

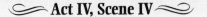

Act IV, Scene IV

Scene Synopsis

This scene is often cut from staged productions. No, you still need to read it. Lord Capulet sends the Nurse to wake up Juliet. Good Luck!

Scene IV
Hall in Capulet's house.

Enter LADY CAPULET and NURSE

LADY CAPULET
Hold, take these keys, and fetch more spices, Nurse.

NURSE
They call for dates and quinces in the pastry.

Enter CAPULET

CAPULET
Come, stir, stir, stir! the second cock hath crow'd,
The curfew bell hath rung, 'tis three o'clock:
Look to the baked meats, good Angelica:
Spare not for the cost.

Apparently, L.C. is still dressed as a housewife and giving orders around the kitchen.

NURSE
Go, you cot-quean, go,
Get you to bed; faith, You'll be sick tomorrow
For this night's watching.

"cot-quean": a man who plays housewife (or Lord Capulet has chosen an alternative lifestyle - Paris, look out!).

CAPULET
No, not a whit: what! I have watch'd ere now
All night for lesser cause, and ne'er been sick.

Translation: "Not your business, girl!"

LADY CAPULET
Ay, you have been a mouse-hunt in your time;
But I will watch you from such watching now.

"mouse-hunt": a weasel who hunts at night or a womanizer (she hopes!).

Exeunt LADY CAPULET and NURSE

CAPULET
A jealous hood, a jealous hood!

L.C. thinks Lady Capulet is jealous of his apron.

Enter three or four SERVINGMEN, with spits, logs, and baskets

Uh, oh. The brain-trust is here.

Now, fellow,
What is there?

FIRST SERVINGMAN
Things for the cook, sir; but I know not what.

CAPULET
Make haste, make haste.

Exit FIRST SERVINGMAN
Sirrah, fetch drier logs:
Call Peter, he will show thee where they are.

SECOND SERVINGMAN
I have a head, sir, that will find out logs,
And never trouble Peter for the matter.

Translation: "Relax, Miss Thang, I can do it myself."

Exit

CAPULET

Mass, and well said; a merry whoreson, ha!
Thou shalt be loggerhead. Good faith, 'tis day:
The County will be here with music straight,
For so he said he would: I hear him near.

"Mass; whoreson": joking terms of familiarity.

[Music within.]

He's so possessive of Paris!

Nurse! Wife! What, ho! What, Nurse, I say!

Enter NURSE

Go waken Juliet, go and trim her up;
I'll go and chat with Paris: hie, make haste,
Make haste; the bridegroom he is come already:
Make haste, I say.

Make sure you just "chat," L.C.

Exeunt

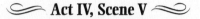

Act IV, Scene V

Scene Synopsis

The theme of marriage/death is emphasized as wedding plans turn to funeral plans when the Nurse finds Juliet apparently dead.

Scene V
Juliet's chamber.

Enter NURSE

NURSE

Mistress! what, mistress! Juliet! fast, I warrant her, she:
Why, lamb! why, lady! fie, you slug-abed!
Why, love, I say! madam! sweetheart! why, bride!
What, not a word? you take your pennyworths now;
Sleep for a week; for the next night, I warrant,
The County Paris hath set up his rest,
That you shall rest but little. God forgive me,
Marry, and amen, how sound is she asleep!
I must needs wake her. Madam, madam, madam!
Ay, let the County take you in your bed;
He'll fright you up, i' faith. Will it not be?

Even knowing what she knows, the Nurse can't resist making a bawdy comment about the wedding night.

[Undraws the curtains.]

What, dress'd! and in your clothes! and down again!
I must needs wake you; Lady! lady! lady!
Alas, alas! Help, help! my lady's dead!
O, well-a-day, that ever I was born!
Some aqua vitae, ho! My lord! my lady!

"aqua vitae": a refreshing spirit (no, not a man's aftershave!).

Enter LADY CAPULET

LADY CAPULET

What noise is here?

NURSE

O lamentable day!

LADY CAPULET

What is the matter?

She probably thinks the problem concerns Lord C!

NURSE

Look, look! O heavy day!

LADY CAPULET

O me, O me! My child, my only life,
Revive, look up, or I will die with thee!
Help, help! Call help.

Now she cares - a little late.

Enter CAPULET

CAPULET

For shame, bring Juliet forth; her lord is come.

If they want help, what's he/she doing here?

NURSE

She's dead, deceased, she's dead; alack the day!

LADY CAPULET

Alack the day, she's dead, she's dead, she's dead!

Everybody got that? She's dead.

CAPULET

Ha! let me see her: out, alas! she's cold:
Her blood is settled, and her joints are stiff;
Life and these lips have long been separated:
Death lies on her like an untimely frost
Upon the sweetest flower of all the field.

The Capulets' reaction is understandable. Psychologists have long said that there is no greater grief a human can experience than that of a parent losing a child.

NURSE

O lamentable day!

LADY CAPULET

O woeful time!

CAPULET

Death, that hath ta'en her hence to make me wail,
Ties up my tongue, and will not let me speak.

It took Juliet's apparent death to shut him up - should've thought of that earlier.

Enter FRIAR LAURENCE and PARIS, with MUSICIANS

FRIAR LAURENCE

Come, is the bride ready to go to church?

Double-meaning: to go to church, yes, but to be buried, not married.

CAPULET

Ready to go, but never to return.
O son! the night before thy wedding day
Hath Death lain with thy wife. There she lies,
Flower as she was, deflowered by him.
Death is my son-in-law, Death is my heir;
My daughter he hath wedded: I will die,
And leave him all; life, living, all is Death's.

PARIS

Have I thought long to see this morning's face,
And doth it give me such a sight as this?

That's it, Paris - think only of yourself at a time like this. Schmuck!

LADY CAPULET

Accursed, unhappy, wretched, hateful day!
Most miserable hour that e'er time saw
In lasting labour of his pilgrimage!
But one, poor one, one poor and loving child,
But one thing to rejoice and solace in,
And cruel Death hath catch'd it from my sight!

NURSE

O woe! O woeful, woeful, woeful day!
Most lamentable day, most woeful day,
That ever, ever, I did yet behold!
O day! O day! O day! O hateful day!
Never was seen so black a day as this:
O woeful day, O woeful day!

PARIS

Beguiled, divorced, wronged, spited, slain!
Most detestable Death, by thee beguil'd,
By cruel cruel thee quite overthrown!
O love! O life! not life, but love in death!

Hey, Paris has caught on to the theme!

CAPULET

Despised, distressed, hated, martyr'd, kill'd!
Uncomfortable time, why cam'st thou now
To murder, murder our solemnity?
O child! O child! my soul, and not my child!
Dead art thou! Alack! my child is dead;
And with my child my joys are buried.

FRIAR LAURENCE

Peace, ho, for shame! confusion's cure lives not
In these confusions. Heaven and yourself
Had part in this fair maid; now heaven hath all,
And all the better is it for the maid:
Your part in her you could not keep from death,
But heaven keeps his part in eternal life.
The most you sought was her promotion;
For 'twas your heaven she should be advanced:
And weep ye now, seeing she is advanced
Above the clouds, as high as heaven itself?
O, in this love, you love your child so ill,
That you run mad, seeing that she is well:
She's not well married that lives married long;
But she's best married that dies married young.
Dry up your tears, and stick your rosemary
On this fair corse; and, as the custom is,
In all her best array bear her to church:
For though fond nature bids us all lament,
Yet nature's tears are reason's merriment.

Translation: "This is not your fault."

"rosemary": an herb, symbolic of remembrance.

CAPULET

All things that we ordained festival,
Turn from their office to black funeral;
Our instruments to melancholy bells,
Our wedding cheer to a sad burial feast,
Our solemn hymns to sullen dirges change,
Our bridal flowers serve for a buried corse,
And all things change them to the contrary.

L.C. catches on: notice how Shakespeare reiterates the theme: festival/funeral, wedding cheer/burial feast, solemn hymns/sullen dirges, bridal flowers/buried corse (corpse).

FRIAR LAURENCE

Sir, go you in; and, madam, go with him;
And go, Sir Paris; everyone prepare
To follow this fair corse unto her grave:

The heavens do lour upon you for some ill;
Move them no more by crossing their high will.

Exeunt CAPULET, LADY CAPULET, PARIS, and FRIAR LAURENCE

FIRST MUSICIAN

Faith, we may put up our pipes, and be gone.

NURSE

Honest good fellows, ah, put up, put up;
For, well you know, this is a pitiful case.

Exit

FIRST MUSICIAN

Ay, by my troth, the case may be amended.

Enter PETER

PETER

Musicians, O, musicians, 'Heart's ease, Heart's
ease:' O, an you will have me live, play 'Heart's ease.'

FIRST MUSICIAN

Why 'Heart's ease?'

PETER

O, musicians, because my heart itself plays 'My
heart is full of woe: ' O, play me some merry dump,
to comfort me.

FIRST MUSICIAN

Not a dump we; 'tis no time to play now.

PETER

You will not, then?

FIRST MUSICIAN

No.

PETER

I will then give it you soundly.

FIRST MUSICIAN

What will you give us?

PETER

No money, on my faith, but the gleek;
I will give you the minstrel.

FIRST MUSICIAN

Then I will give you the serving-creature.

PETER

Then will I lay the serving-creature's dagger on
your pate. I will carry no crotchets: I'll *re* you,
I'll *fa* you; do you note me?

FIRST MUSICIAN

An you *re* us and *fa* us, you note us.

SECOND MUSICIAN

Pray you, put up your dagger, and put out your wit.

"lour": lower, as in the heavens do frown and darken upon you.

The Second Quarto reads: "Enter Will Kemp." Kemp was one of the Elizabethan era's most famous stage clowns and a low-comedian in Shakespeare's own acting company.

"dump": a sad song (not something that happens in the bathroom).

Peter has finally found someone to pick on; the musicians grow tired of him.

"gleek, minstrel": insulting terms.

"Peter Pun": pate (head)/pate, crotchets (perverse conceit)/quarter notes.

"*re/fa*": a pun on the musical phrase "*do re me.*"

PETER

Then have at you with my wit! I will dry-beat you
with an iron wit, and put up my iron dagger. Answer
me like men:
'When griping grief the heart doth wound,
And doleful dumps the mind oppress,
Then music with her silver sound'--
why 'silver sound'? why 'music with her silver
sound'? What say you, Simon Catling?

Peter gets lost in mid-thought and becomes confused.

MUSICIAN

Marry, sir, because silver hath a sweet sound.

PETER

Pretty! What say you, Hugh Rebeck?

Peter makes up last names: Catling, Rebeck, and Soundpost are all musical instruments or parts.

SECOND MUSICIAN

I say 'silver sound,' because musicians sound for silver.

PETER

Pretty too! What say you, James Soundpost?

THIRD MUSICIAN

Faith, I know not what to say.

Translation: "Someone shut Peter up!"

PETER

O, I cry you mercy; you are the singer: I will say
for you. It is 'music with her silver sound,'
because musicians have no gold for sounding:
'Then music with her silver sound
With speedy help doth lend redress.'

Peter tries to sound intelligent, but alas, no go.

Exit

FIRST MUSICIAN

What a pestilent knave is this same!

SECOND MUSICIAN

Hang him, Jack! Come, we'll in here; tarry for the
mourners, and stay dinner.

Like modern-day artists, free food and they're there.

Exeunt

Act IV Notes

Act IV Notes

Act IV Notes

Romeo and Juliet

～ Act V, Scene I ～

Scene Synopsis

Romeo's home-peep, Balthasar, tells Romeo of Juliet's death. Anguished, Romeo buys poison from an apothecary (or pharmacist) to kill himself.

Scene I
Mantua. A street.

Enter ROMEO

ROMEO

> If I may trust the flattering truth of sleep,
> My dreams presage some joyful news at hand:
> My bosom's lord sits lightly in his throne;
> And all this day an unaccustom'd spirit
> Lifts me above the ground with cheerful thoughts.
> I dreamt my lady came and found me dead--
> Strange dream, that gives a dead man leave
> to think!—
> And breathed such life with kisses in my lips,
> That I revived, and was an emperor.
> Ah me! how sweet is love itself possess'd,
> When but love's shadows are so rich in joy!

Enter BALTHASAR, booted

> News from Verona!--How now, Balthasar!
> Dost thou not bring me letters from the Friar?
> How doth my lady? Is my father well?
> How fares my Juliet? that I ask again;
> For nothing can be ill, if she be well.

BALTHASAR

> Then she is well, and nothing can be ill:
> Her body sleeps in Capel's monument,
> And her immortal part with angels lives.
> I saw her laid low in her kindred's vault,
> And presently took post to tell it you:
> O, pardon me for bringing these ill news,
> Since you did leave it for my office, sir.

ROMEO

> Is it e'en so? then I defy you, stars!
> Thou know'st my lodging: get me ink and paper,
> And hire posthorses; I will hence tonight.

BALTHASAR

> I do beseech you, sir, have patience:
> Your looks are pale and wild, and do import
> Some misadventure.

ROMEO

> Tush, thou art deceived:
> Leave me, and do the thing I bid thee do.
> Hast thou no letters to me from the Friar?

"bosom's lord": his heart.

Romeo should have had his own call-in fortune telling business with dreams like this! Yes, it's foreshadowing.

"booted": as in dressed in horse riding boots.

Romeo asks four questions without waiting to hear the answer to the first one - don't you hate it when people do that?

Hmmm. . .Balthasar has an interesting interpretation of "well" - she's dead!

"took post": write a letter to post (or mail).

Ancient Greek tradition decreed that a messenger bearing bad news should be killed.

Recall the Chorus guy referring to R & J as "star-crossed" or ill-fated.

And you're surprised by this kind of reaction?

"tush": blow it off; no prob, Bob.

Ah, the letters. . .a key element in this fateful tragedy. Watch for all letters.

BALTHASAR

    No, my good lord.

ROMEO

    No matter: get thee gone,
    And hire those horses; I'll be with thee straight.

                      "straight": shortly; soon.

Exit BALTHASAR

    Well, Juliet, I will lie with thee tonight.
    Let's see for means: O mischief, thou art swift
    To enter in the thoughts of desperate men!
    I do remember an apothecary,--
    And hereabouts he dwells,--which late I noted
    In tatter'd weeds, with overwhelming brows,
    Culling of simples; meagre were his looks,
    Sharp misery had worn him to the bones:
    And in his needy shop a tortoise hung,
    An alligator stuff'd, and other skins
    Of ill-shaped fishes; and about his shelves
    A beggarly account of empty boxes,
    Green earthen pots, bladders and musty seeds,
    Remnants of packthread and old cakes of roses,
    Were thinly scatter'd, to make up a show.
    Noting this penury, to myself I said
    'An if a man did need a poison now,
    Whose sale is present death in Mantua,
    Here lives a caitiff wretch would sell it him.'
    O, this same thought did but forerun my need;
    And this same needy man must sell it me.
    As I remember, this should be the house.
    Being holiday, the beggar's shop is shut.
    What, ho! apothecary!

Romeo looks for and finds a poor apothecary or pharmacist who, because he needs money, will sell poison to someone without hesitation.

"simples": a concoction of a few medicinal herbs.

Turtle shells and other common items found in nature were used, as Father Larry does for Juliet, to make medicine, perfumes, beauty aids, and soap.

"a show": to make people think he was a successful apothecary.

"holiday": probably Sunday, as this is Catholic Italy.

Enter APOTHECARY

APOTHECARY

    Who calls so loud?

ROMEO

    Come hither, man. I see that thou art poor:
    Hold, there is forty ducats: let me have
    A dram of poison, such soon-speeding gear
    As will disperse itself through all the veins
    That the life-weary taker may fall dead
    And that the trunk may be discharged of breath
    As violently as hasty powder fired
    Doth hurry from the fatal cannon's womb.

Romeo makes a drug deal on a corner in Mantua.

APOTHECARY

    Such mortal drugs I have; but Mantua's law
    Is death to any he that utters them.

The man needs Romeo's money, but it's against the law to sell poison.

ROMEO

    Art thou so bare and full of wretchedness,
    And fear'st to die? famine is in thy cheeks,
    Need and oppression starveth in thy eyes,

Contempt and beggary hangs upon thy back;
The world is not thy friend nor the world's law;
The world affords no law to make thee rich;
Then be not poor, but break it, and take this.

APOTHECARY

My poverty, but not my will, consents.

ROMEO

I pay thy poverty, and not thy will.

APOTHECARY

Put this in any liquid thing you will,
And drink it off; and, if you had the strength
Of twenty men, it would dispatch you straight.

ROMEO

There is thy gold, worse poison to men's souls,
Doing more murders in this loathsome world,
Than these poor compounds that thou mayst not sell.
I sell thee poison; thou hast sold me none.
Farewell: buy food, and get thyself in flesh.
Come, cordial and not poison, go with me
To Juliet's grave; for there must I use thee.

Exeunt

Ah, the power of rhetoric: money talks.

Translation: "This is some killer (literally) stuff!"

Romeo turned philosopher: he compares man's lust for money with the "compound" of poison.

❦ Act V, Scene II ❧

Scene Synopsis

Father Larry learns that his plan, once more, has hit a snag. The letter – telling Romeo that Juliet is *not* dead - was never delivered. Ah, miscommunications!

Scene II
Friar Laurence's cell.

Enter FRIAR JOHN

FRIAR JOHN

Holy Franciscan Friar! brother, ho!

Enter FRIAR LAURENCE

FRIAR LAURENCE

This same should be the voice of Friar John.
Welcome from Mantua: what says Romeo?
Or, if his mind be writ, give me his letter.

FRIAR JOHN

Going to find a barefoot brother out
One of our order, to associate me,
Here in this city visiting the sick,
And finding him, the searchers of the town,
Suspecting that we both were in a house
Where the infectious pestilence did reign,
Seal'd up the doors, and would not let us forth;
So that my speed to Mantua there was stay'd.

You would think that entrusting a letter to a priest would be safe.

"his mind be writ": if he answered my letter in writing.

Why does a brother have to be barefoot?

"the sick": Friar John and others of his priestly order were tending to victims of the plague, an infectious disease that devastated thousands in England and Europe at this time.

FRIAR LAURENCE

> Who bare my letter, then, to Romeo?

FRIAR JOHN

> I could not send it,—here it is again,—
> Nor get a messenger to bring it thee,
> So fearful were they of infection.

Because of the deadly nature of the plague, people and sometimes entire towns were quarantined to protect others. How is this ironic for R & J?

FRIAR LAURENCE

> Unhappy fortune! by my brotherhood,
> The letter was not nice but full of charge
> Of dear import, and the neglecting it
> May do much danger. Friar John, go hence;
> Get me an iron crow, and bring it straight
> Unto my cell.

"nice": trivial, of little importance.

"iron crow": crowbar (no, not a steel bird!).

FRIAR JOHN

> Brother, I'll go and bring it thee.

Father Larry wants a crowbar to lift the top of Juliet's tomb (or to change a flat tire on the way?).

Exit

FRIAR LAURENCE

> Now must I to the monument alone;
> Within this three hours will fair Juliet wake:
> She will beshrew me much that Romeo
> Hath had no notice of these accidents;
> But I will write again to Mantua,
> And keep her at my cell till Romeo come;
> Poor living corse, closed in a dead man's tomb!

Translation: "Oops, my bad!"

"beshrew": be angry.

Juliet will stay at Larry's crib. Shouldn't he have already thought about this?

Exit

∽ Act V, Scene III ∽

Scene Synopsis

Final scene, the climax. For Shakespeare, that means dead bodies all over the place! Romeo kills Paris and himself. Not to be outdone or left alone, Juliet kills herself, too. The feuding families resolve their differences. Harmony is restored, at a great price. The youth sets the adult world straight.

Scene III
A churchyard; in it a tomb belonging to the Capulets.

Enter PARIS, and his PAGE bearing flowers and a torch

PARIS

> Give me thy torch, boy: hence, and stand aloof:
> Yet put it out, for I would not be seen.
> Under yond yew trees lay thee all along,
> Holding thine ear close to the hollow ground;
> So shall no foot upon the churchyard tread,
> Being loose, unfirm, with digging up of graves,
> But thou shalt hear it: whistle then to me,
> As signal that thou hear'st something approach.
> Give me those flowers. Do as I bid thee, go.

Cemeteries were scary places for Elizabethans (today, too!). Belief in ghosts, magic, and the supernatural were strong and widespread throughout the social classes.

PAGE

> [*Aside.*] I am almost afraid to stand alone
> Here in the churchyard; yet I will adventure.
>
> [*Retires.*]

Panty-waist coward! What a wuss!

PARIS

Sweet flower, with flowers thy bridal bed I strew,--
O woe! thy canopy is dust and stones;--
Which with sweet water nightly I will dew,
Or, wanting that, with tears distill'd by moans:
The obsequies that I for thee will keep
Nightly shall be to strew thy grave and weep.

[The PAGE whistles.]

The boy gives warning something doth approach.
What cursed foot wanders this way to-night,
To cross my obsequies and true love's rite?
What with a torch! muffle me, night, awhile.

[Retires.]

Enter ROMEO and BALTHASAR, with a torch, mattock, & crowbar

ROMEO

Give me that mattock and the wrenching iron.
Hold, take this letter; early in the morning
See thou deliver it to my lord and father.
Give me the light: upon thy life, I charge thee,
Whate'er thou hear'st or seest, stand all aloof,
And do not interrupt me in my course.
Why I descend into this bed of death,
Is partly to behold my lady's face;
But chiefly to take thence from her dead finger
A precious ring, a ring that I must use
In dear employment: therefore hence, be gone:
But if thou, jealous, dost return to pry
In what I farther shall intend to do,
By heaven, I will tear thee joint by joint
And strew this hungry churchyard with thy limbs:
The time and my intents are savage-wild,
More fierce and more inexorable far
Than empty tigers or the roaring sea.

BALTHASAR

I will be gone, sir, and not trouble you.

ROMEO

So shalt thou show me friendship. Take thou that:
Live, and be prosperous: and farewell, good fellow.

BALTHASAR

[Aside.] For all this same, I'll hide me hereabout:
His looks I fear, and his intents I doubt.

[Retires.]

ROMEO

Thou detestable maw, thou womb of death,
Gorged with the dearest morsel of the earth,
Thus I enforce thy rotten jaws to open,
And, in despite, I'll cram thee with more food!

[Opens the tomb.]

Paris is clearly a graduate of Father Larry's House of Rhyme.

"obsequies": honoring rites, in this case, perfume or flowers for Juliet's grave.

Yeah, that "something" is the Grim Reaper, Paris!

Fire-on-a-stick, an axe (mattock), and a crowbar - what everyone takes to visit a cemetery.

Romeo, the grave robber.

Whoa! Here's a different side of Romeo - a whole new meaning to "raging" hormone.

"empty": hungry; "empty" stomach.

Good answer!

Romeo gives Balthasar money.

Now that's friendship!

"maw": jaws of a hungry beast.

"womb of death": Juliet's tomb.

Shakespeare uses personification for Romeo's description of the tomb.

"more food": Romeo's dead body.

PARIS

This is that banish'd haughty Montague,
That murder'd my love's cousin, with which grief,
It is supposed, the fair creature died;
And here is come to do some villainous shame
To the dead bodies: I will apprehend him.

[Comes forward.]

Stop thy unhallow'd toil, vile Montague!
Can vengeance be pursued further than death?
Condemned villain, I do apprehend thee:
Obey, and go with me; for thou must die.

ROMEO

I must indeed; and therefore came I hither.
Good gentle youth, tempt not a desperate man;
Fly hence, and leave me: think upon these gone;
Let them affright thee. I beseech thee, youth,
Put not another sin upon my head,
By urging me to fury: O, be gone!
By heaven, I love thee better than myself;
For I come hither arm'd against myself:
Stay not, be gone; live, and hereafter say,
A madman's mercy bid thee run away.

PARIS

I do defy thy conjuration,
And apprehend thee for a felon here.

ROMEO

Wilt thou provoke me? then have at thee, boy!

[They fight.]

PAGE

O Lord, they fight! I will go call the watch.

Exit

PARIS

O, I am slain!

[Falls.]

If thou be merciful,
Open the tomb, lay me with Juliet.

[Dies.]

ROMEO

In faith, I will. Let me peruse this face.
Mercutio's kinsman, noble County Paris!
What said my man, when my betossed soul
Did not attend him as we rode? I think
He told me Paris should have married Juliet:
Said he not so? or did I dream it so?
Or am I mad, hearing him talk of Juliet,
To think it was so? O, give me thy hand,
One writ with me in sour misfortune's book!
I'll bury thee in a triumphant grave;

Translation: "Look, it's Romeo!"

"apprehend": arrest.

Paris interprets Romeo's actions as purposefully defacing a Capulet grave.

Romeo warns Paris: leave me alone or I'll have to kill you.

Romeo wants to kill himself, not Paris.

Apparently Paris is not as smart as Balthasar.

Because of the darkness, Romeo has no idea who he's fighting.

A trusty servant is fleet of foot.

One of the shortest death speeches in all of Shakespeare.

In his highly-emotional state, Romeo tries to remember why Paris would be here and care about Juliet's grave.

A grave? O no! a lantern, slaughter'd youth,
For here lies Juliet, and her beauty makes
This vault a feasting presence full of light.
Death, lie thou there, by a dead man interr'd.

[Laying PARIS in the tomb.]

How oft when men are at the point of death
Have they been merry! which their keepers call
A lightning before death: O, how may I
Call this a lightning? O my love! my wife!
Death, that hath suck'd the honey of thy breath,
Hath had no power yet upon thy beauty:
Thou art not conquer'd; beauty's ensign yet
Is crimson in thy lips and in thy cheeks,
And death's pale flag is not advanced there.
Tybalt, liest thou there in thy bloody sheet?
O, what more favour can I do to thee,
Than with that hand that cut thy youth in twain
To sunder his that was thine enemy?
Forgive me, cousin! Ah, dear Juliet,
Why art thou yet so fair? shall I believe
That unsubstantial Death is amorous,
And that the lean abhorred monster keeps
Thee here in dark to be his paramour?
For fear of that, I still will stay with thee;
And never from this palace of dim night
Depart again: here, here will I remain
With worms that are thy chambermaids; O, here
Will I set up my everlasting rest,
And shake the yoke of inauspicious stars
From this world-wearied flesh. Eyes, look your last!
Arms, take your last embrace! and, lips, O you
The doors of breath, seal with a righteous kiss
A dateless bargain to engrossing death!
Come, bitter conduct, come, unsavoury guide!
Thou desperate pilot, now at once run on
The dashing rocks thy seasick weary bark!
Here's to my love!

[Drinks.]

O true apothecary!
Thy drugs are quick. Thus with a kiss I die.

[Falls.]

***Enter, at the other end of the churchyard, FRIAR
LAURENCE, with a lantern, crow, and spade***

FRIAR LAURENCE

Saint Francis be my speed! how oft to-night
Have my old feet stumbled at graves! Who's there?

BALTHASAR

Here's one, a friend, and one that knows you well.

In Zeffirelli's '68 film, Juliet's tomb was lit with a few torches; however, Luhrmann's '96 film illuminated Juliet's tomb with hundreds of candles. Which director comes closest to realizing Shakespeare's "feasting presence full of light"?

Romeo's comments about that mysterious moment before death fascinated physicians, philosophers, and theologians.

Remember the heat Benny spoke of earlier? Tybalt could be found in this tomb, in a bloody sheet. PeeeeYewwwwwwww!

"monster": death.

"paramour": a lover. (Man, what a one-track mind, Romeo!)

"engrossing": a commercial term for monopolizing a commodity or goods in trade.

"drugs are quick": in the '96 film, this line was said at the party in Act I. Romeo said the line after taking a pill (Ecstasy?) given to him by Mercutio. Hmmm, a post-modern adaptation of our poet's text.

You think you're stumbling now? Just wait, Father Larry!

FRIAR LAURENCE

    Bliss be upon you! Tell me, good my friend,
    What torch is yond, that vainly lends his light
    To grubs and eyeless skulls? as I discern,
    It burneth in the Capel's monument.

BALTHASAR

    It doth so, holy sir; and there's my master,
    One that you love.

FRIAR LAURENCE

    Who is it?

BALTHASAR

    Romeo.

FRIAR LAURENCE

    How long hath he been there?

BALTHASAR

    Full half an hour.

FRIAR LAURENCE

    Go with me to the vault.

BALTHASAR

    I dare not, sir
    My master knows not but I am gone hence;
    And fearfully did menace me with death,
    If I did stay to look on his intents.

FRIAR LAURENCE

    Stay, then; I'll go alone. Fear comes upon me:
    O, much I fear some ill unthrifty thing.

BALTHASAR

    As I did sleep under this yew tree here,
    I dreamt my master and another fought,
    And that my master slew him.

FRIAR LAURENCE

    Romeo!

    [Advances.]

    Alack, alack, what blood is this, which stains
    The stony entrance of this sepulchre?
    What mean these masterless and gory swords
    To lie discolour'd by this place of peace?

    [Enters the tomb.]

    Romeo! O, pale! Who else? what, Paris too?
    And steep'd in blood? Ah, what an unkind hour
    Is guilty of this lamentable chance!
    The lady stirs.

    [JULIET wakes.]

JULIET

    O comfortable friar! where is my lord?
    I do remember well where I should be,
    And there I am. Where is my Romeo?

"Capel's": Capulet's tomb.

The next seven lines (from "It doth" to "Go with me. . . ") are shared, creating three lines of iambic pentameter, and they are intended to be spoken quickly.

Now, how many people that Larry loves, let alone knows, would be in a cemetery, at night, around the Capulet's tomb?

Hey, Balthasar *was* listening.

Trust those holy instincts, Father!

Well, maybe not.

Father Larry finds Romeo's and Paris' swords and subsequent blood around the entrance of the tomb.

A little late here, Father.

(Father Larry thinks: "Uh. . .well. . . you see, the funniest thing happened. Remember that letter I was to send to Romeo. . .?")

[Noise within.]

FRIAR LAURENCE

> I hear some noise. Lady, come from that nest
> Of death, contagion, and unnatural sleep:
> A greater power than we can contradict
> Hath thwarted our intents. Come, come away.
> Thy husband in thy bosom there lies dead;
> And Paris too. Come, I'll dispose of thee
> Among a sisterhood of holy nuns:
> Stay not to question, for the watch is coming;
> Come, go, good Juliet,

> *[Noise again.]*

> I dare no longer stay.

JULIET

> Go, get thee hence, for I will not away.

Exit FRIAR LAURENCE

> What's here? a cup, closed in my true love's hand?
> Poison, I see, hath been his timeless end:
> O churl! drunk all, and left no friendly drop
> To help me after? I will kiss thy lips;
> Haply some poison yet doth hang on them,
> To make me die with a restorative.

> *[Kisses him.]*

> Thy lips are warm.

FIRST WATCHMAN

> *[Within.]* Lead, boy: which way?

JULIET

> Yea, noise? then I'll be brief. O happy dagger!

> *[Snatching ROMEO's dagger.]*

> This is thy sheath;

> *[Stabs herself.]*

> there rust, and let me die.

> *[Falls on ROMEO's body, and dies.]*

Enter WATCH, with the PAGE of PARIS

PAGE

> This is the place; there, where the torch doth burn.

FIRST WATCHMAN

> The ground is bloody; search about the churchyard:
> Go, some of you, whoe'er you find attach.
> Pitiful sight! here lies the County slain,
> And Juliet bleeding, warm, and newly dead,
> Who here hath lain this two days buried.
> Go, tell the Prince: run to the Capulets:
> Raise up the Montagues: some others search:
> We see the ground whereon these woes do lie;
> But the true ground of all these piteous woes
> We cannot without circumstance descry.

After two days, I bet Juliet has to use the bathroom.

Well, he broke that news gently!

Juliet chooses death over life as a nun.

Where's he going?

"churl": a miserly, low-life.

Juliet kisses Romeo in hopes of sharing the deadly poison.

"happy dagger": a continuation of the opposition theme.

Where has this "Watch" been all this time?

"Watchman": the Elizabethan equivalent of a security guard.

The Watch orders others to search the cemetery for clues to these mysteries of the dead men and newly-stabbed Juliet.

"descry": discern.

Re-enter some of the WATCH, with BALTHASAR

SECOND WATCHMAN
> Here's Romeo's man; we found him in the churchyard.

FIRST WATCHMAN
> Hold him in safety, till the Prince come hither.

Re-enter others of the WATCH, with FRIAR LAURENCE

THIRD WATCHMAN
> Here is a friar, that trembles, sighs and weeps:
> We took this mattock and this spade from him,
> As he was coming from this churchyard side.

FIRST WATCHMAN
> A great suspicion: stay the friar too.

Enter the PRINCE and ATTENDANTS

PRINCE
> What misadventure is so early up,
> That calls our person from our morning rest?

Enter CAPULET, LADY CAPULET, and others

CAPULET
> What should it be, that is so shrieked abroad?

LADY CAPULET
> O the people in the street cry 'Romeo.'
> Some 'Juliet,' and some 'Paris,' and all run,
> With open outcry toward our monument.

PRINCE
> What fear is this which startles in our ears?

FIRST WATCHMAN
> Sovereign, here lies the County Paris slain;
> And Romeo dead; and Juliet, dead before,
> Warm and new kill'd.

PRINCE
> Search, seek, and know how this foul murder comes.

FIRST WATCHMAN
> Here is a friar, and slaughter'd Romeo's man;
> With instruments upon them, fit to open
> These dead men's tombs.

CAPULET
> O heavens! O wife, look how our daughter bleeds!
> This dagger hath mista'en--for, lo, his house
> Is empty on the back of Montague,—
> And it mis-sheathed in my daughter's bosom!

LADY CAPULET
> O me! this sight of death is as a bell,
> That warns my old age to a sepulchre.

Enter MONTAGUE and others

PRINCE
> Come, Montague; for thou art early up,
> To see thy son and heir more early down.

Oh, now they are *two* Watches asleep at the wheel!

Three? Where have these guys been all night?

Spade? Where did Larry get the shovel?

See? Carrying an axe and a shovel in a cemetery is suspicious, then and now!

Oh, oh.

He's mad because it's early in the morning? Just wait, Prince, it's about to get really good.

Ah, Lord Capulet. . .every serious situation needs a clown!

Look in the tomb and see what you see, old man!

Hmmm. . .there's a clue in there somewhere.

Like any good detective; just the facts, ma'am.

Oh, now look who's getting emotional!

Lady C. is reminded of her own mortality.

Again, the theme: "early up/early down."

MONTAGUE

Alas, my liege, my wife is dead tonight;
Grief of my son's exile hath stopp'd her breath:
What further woe conspires against mine age?

PRINCE

Look, and thou shalt see.

MONTAGUE

O thou untaught! what manners is in this?
To press before thy father to a grave?

PRINCE

Seal up the mouth of outrage for a while,
Till we can clear these ambiguities,
And know their spring, their head, their
true descent;
And then will I be general of your woes,
And lead you even to death: meantime forbear,
And let mischance be slave to patience.
Bring forth the parties of suspicion.

FRIAR LAURENCE

I am the greatest, able to do least,
Yet most suspected, as the time and place
Doth make against me of this direful murder;
And here I stand, both to impeach and purge
Myself condemned and myself excused.

PRINCE

Then say at once what thou dost know in this.

FRIAR LAURENCE

I will be brief, for my short date of breath
Is not so long as is a tedious tale.
Romeo, there dead, was husband to that Juliet;
And she, there dead, that Romeo's faithful wife:
I married them; and their stol'n marriage day
Was Tybalt's doomsday, whose untimely death
Banish'd the new-made bridegroom from the city,
For whom, and not for Tybalt, Juliet pined.
You, to remove that siege of grief from her,
Betroth'd and would have married her perforce
To County Paris: then comes she to me,
And, with wild looks, bid me devise some mean
To rid her from this second marriage,
Or in my cell there would she kill herself.
Then gave I her, so tutor'd by my art,
A sleeping potion; which so took effect
As I intended, for it wrought on her
The form of death: meantime I writ to Romeo,
That he should hither come as this dire night,
To help to take her from her borrow'd grave,
Being the time the potion's force should cease.
But he which bore my letter, Friar John,
Was stay'd by accident, and yesternight

So, a quick count of the dead:
1) Mercutio, 2) Tybalt, 3) Paris,
4) Romeo, 5) Juliet, and
6) Lady Montague -
that's our boy Will!

Translation: "What do you wanna
do - kill me?"

What the Prince is saying: "Chill
a minute, let me get to the
bottom of this."

Again, the theme: greatest/least,
impeach/purge,
condemned/excused.

Father Larry's definition of "brief"
is a bit long winded:
41 lines!?!

The Prince is keeping score:
"I married them": first mistake.

Gave drugs to Juliet: that's two.

Deception of family: three points.

Postal delay: that's four.

Return'd my letter back. Then all alone
At the prefixed hour of her waking,
Came I to take her from her kindred's vault;
Meaning to keep her closely at my cell,
Till I conveniently could send to Romeo:
But when I came, some minute ere the time
Of her awakening, here untimely lay
The noble Paris and true Romeo dead.
She wakes; and I entreated her come forth,
And bear this work of heaven with patience:
But then a noise did scare me from the tomb;
And she, too desperate, would not go with me,
But, as it seems, did violence on herself.
All this I know; and to the marriage
Her Nurse is privy: and, if aught in this
Miscarried by my fault, let my old life
Be sacrificed, some hour before his time,
Unto the rigour of severest law.

PRINCE

We still have known thee for a holy man.
Where's Romeo's man? what can he say in this?

BALTHASAR

I brought my master news of Juliet's death;
And then in post he came from Mantua
To this same place, to this same monument.
This letter he early bid me give his father,
And threatened me with death, going in the vault,
If I departed not and left him there.

PRINCE

Give me the letter; I will look on it.
Where is the County's Page, that raised the watch?
Sirrah, what made your master in this place?

PAGE

He came with flowers to strew his lady's grave;
And bid me stand aloof, and so I did:
Anon comes one with light to ope the tomb;
And by and by my master drew on him;
And then I ran away to call the watch.

PRINCE

This letter doth make good the Friar's words,
Their course of love, the tidings of her death:
And here he writes that he did buy a poison
Of a poor pothecary, and therewithal
Came to this vault to die, and lie with Juliet.
Where be these enemies? Capulet! Montague!
See, what a scourge is laid upon your hate,
That heaven finds means to kill your joys with love.
And I for winking at your discords too
Have lost a brace of kinsmen: all are punish'd.

Late arrival: five mistakes for Larry.

Ran scared like a little girl: six.

Squealed on the Nurse: seven.

Seven mistakes resulting in three deaths - nice job, Father Larry!

Wow! Talk about forgiving!

Balthasar speaks straight to the point.

The Prince has clearly watched too much *NYPD Blue*.

No wonder Romeo was mad: Paris "drew on him" - probably permanent ink and it wouldn't wash off.

Father Larry gets off clean.

Now they're busted.

"winking at your discords": ignoring the severity of the two families' fights.

CAPULET

> O brother Montague, give me thy hand:
> This is my daughter's jointure, for no more
> Can I demand.

Yeah, give me your hand so I can slap you with the other one.

"jointure": dowry.

MONTAGUE

> But I can give thee more:
> For I will raise her statue in pure gold;
> That while Verona by that name is known,
> There shall no figure at such rate be set
> As that of true and faithful Juliet.

This is serious: he's rhyming!

CAPULET

> As rich shall Romeo's by his lady's lie;
> Poor sacrifices of our enmity!

PRINCE

> A glooming peace this morning with it brings;
> The sun, for sorrow, will not show his head:
> Go hence, to have more talk of these sad things;
> Some shall be pardon'd, and some punished:
> For never was a story of more woe
> Than this of Juliet and her Romeo.

Rhyme scheme: "punished is pronounced "pun-ish-Ed" to rhyme with "head."

That's it! You made it! Congrats!

Exeunt

Act V Notes